Manhattan Review

Test Prep & Admissions Consulting

Turbocharge Your GRE: Math Essentials Guide

2nd Edition (December 18th, 2012)

- ☐ *GRE specific math concepts and theory*
- ☐ *Intuitive and graphical explanations of concepts*
- ☐ *Smart Math Shortcuts*
- ☐ *Comprehensive collection of math formulae*
- ☐ *Over 100 practice questions*
- ☐ *Mapped according to the scope of the GRE*

www.manhattanreview.com

Copyright and Terms of Use

Copyright and Trademark

Terms of Use

No Warranties

Limitation on Liability

10-Digit International Standard Book Number: (ISBN: 1-62926-031-2)
13-Digit International Standard Book Number: (ISBN: 978-1-62926-031-0)

Last updated on December 18, 2012.
Manhattan Review, 275 Madison Avenue, Suite 424, New York, NY 10025.
Phone: +1 (212) 316-2000. E-Mail: info@manhattanreview.com. Web: www.manhattanreview.com

About the Turbocharge your GRE Series

The Turbocharge Your GRE series is designed to be clear and comprehensive. It is the set of tools you need to build the success you seek. Manhattan Review has created these guides to lead you through the complexities of the examination and achieve your best possible result. As so many students before you have discovered, our books break down the different test sections in a careful, clear manner and zero in on exactly what you need to know to raise your score. The complete series is designed to be your best GRE test prep companion as you navigate the road to a successful outcome.

- ■ **GRE Math Essentials (ISBN: 978-1-62926-031-0)**
- ☐ **GRE Number Properties (ISBN: 978-1-62926-032-7)**
- ☐ **GRE Arithmetics (ISBN: 978-1-62926-033-4**
- ☐ **GRE Algebra (ISBN: 978-1-62926-034-1**
- ☐ **GRE Geometry (ISBN: 978-1-62926-035-8)**
- ☐ **GRE Word Problems (ISBN: 978-1-62926-036-5)**
- ☐ **GRE Combinatorics & Probability (ISBN: 978-1-62926-037-2)**
- ☐ **GRE Statistics & Data Interpretation (ISBN: 978-1-62926-038-9)**
- ☐ **GRE Reading Comprehension (ISBN: 978-1-62926-039-6)**
- ☐ **GRE Sentence Eqivalence & Text Completion (ISBN: 978-1-62926-040-2)**
- ☐ **GRE Analytical Writing Guide (ISBN: 978-1-62926-041-9)**
- ☐ **GRE Vocabulary Builder (ISBN: 978-1-62926-042-6)**

About the Company

Manhattan Review's origin can be traced directly to an Ivy-League MBA classroom in 1999. While lecturing on advanced quantitative subjects to MBAs at Columbia Business School in New York City, Professor Dr. Joern Meissner was asked by his students to assist their friends, who were frustrated with conventional GMAT preparation options. He started to create original lectures that focused on presenting GMAT content in a coherent and concise manner rather than as a download of voluminous basic knowledge interspersed with so-called "tricks." The new approach immediately proved highly popular with GMAT students, inspiring the birth of Manhattan Review. Over the past 15+ years, Manhattan Review has grown into a multi-national firm, focusing on GMAT, GRE, LSAT, SAT, and TOEFL test prep and tutoring, along with business school, graduate school, and college admissions consulting; application advisory, and essay editing services.

About the Founder

Professor Joern Meissner, the founder and chairman of Manhattan Review, has over twenty-five years of teaching experience in undergraduate and graduate programs at prestigious business schools in the USA, UK, and Germany. He created the original lectures, which are constantly updated by the Manhattan Review Team to reflect the evolving nature of GMAT, GRE, LSAT, SAT, and TOEFL test prep and private tutoring. Professor Meissner received his Ph.D. in Management Science from the Graduate School of Business at Columbia University (Columbia Business School) in New York City and is a recognized authority in the area of Supply Chain Management (SCM), Dynamic Pricing, and Revenue Management. Currently, he holds the position of Full Professor of Supply Chain Management and Pricing Strategy at Kuehne Logistics University in Hamburg, Germany. Professor Meissner is a passionate and enthusiastic teacher. He believes that grasping an idea is only half of the fun; conveying it to others makes it whole. At his previous position at Lancaster University Management School, he taught the MBA Core course in Operations Management and originated three new MBA Electives: Advanced Decision Models, Supply Chain Management, and Revenue Management. He has also lectured at the University of Hamburg, the Leipzig Graduate School of Management (HHL), and the University of Mannheim. Professor Meissner offers a variety of Executive Education courses aimed at business professionals, managers, leaders, and executives who strive for professional and personal growth. He frequently advises companies ranging from Fortune 500 companies to emerging start-ups on various issues related to his research expertise. Please visit his academic homepage www.meiss.com for further information.

Manhattan Review Advantages

▶ **Time Efficiency and Cost Effectiveness**
  – The most limiting factor in test preparation for most people is time.
  – It takes significantly more teaching experience and techniques to prepare a student in less time.
  – Our preparation is tailored for busy professionals. We will teach you what you need to know in the least amount of time.

▶ **High-quality and dedicated instructors who are committed to helping every student reach her/his goals**

▶ **Manhattan Review's team members have combined wisdom of**
  – Academic achievements
  – MBA teaching experience at prestigious business schools in the US and UK
  – Career success

**Visit us at www.ManhattanReview.com and
find out which courses are available close to *you*!**

International Phone Numbers & Official Manhattan Review Websites

Manhattan Headquarters	+1-212-316-2000	www.manhattanreview.com
USA & Canada	+1-800-246-4600	www.manhattanreview.com
Australia	+61-3-9001-6618	www.manhattanreview.com
Austria	+43-720-115-549	www.review.at
Belgium	+32-2-808-5163	www.manhattanreview.be
China	+86-20-2910-1913	www.manhattanreview.cn
Czech Republic	+1-212-316-2000	www.review.cz
France	+33-1-8488-4204	www.review.fr
Germany	+49-89-3803-8856	www.review.de
Greece	+1-212-316-2000	www.review.com.gr
Hong Kong	+852-5808-2704	www.review.hk
Hungary	+1-212-316-2000	www.review.co.hu
India	+1-212-316-2000	www.review.in
Indonesia	+1-212-316-2000	www.manhattanreview.com
Ireland	+1-212-316-2000	www.gmat.ie
Italy	+39-06-9338-7617	www.manhattanreview.it
Japan	+81-3-4589-5125	www.manhattanreview.jp
Malaysia	+1-212-316-2000	www.manhattanreview.com
Netherlands	+31-20-808-4399	www.manhattanreview.nl
Philippines	+1-212-316-2000	www.review.ph
Poland	+1-212-316-2000	www.review.pl
Portugal	+1-212-316-2000	www.review.pt
Russia	+1-212-316-2000	www.manhattanreview.ru
Singapore	+65-3158-2571	www.gmat.sg
South Africa	+1-212-316-2000	www.manhattanreview.co.za
South Korea	+1-212-316-2000	www.manhattanreview.kr
Sweden	+1-212-316-2000	www.gmat.se
Spain	+34-911-876-504	www.review.es
Switzerland	+41-435-080-991	www.review.ch
Taiwan	+1-212-316-2000	www.gmat.tw
Thailand	+66-6-0003-5529	www.manhattanreview.com
United Arab Emirates	+1-212-316-2000	www.manhattanreview.ae
United Kingdom	+44-20-7060-9800	www.manhattanreview.co.uk
Rest of the World	+1-212-316-2000	www.manhattanreview.com

Contents

Chapter 1

Introduction

Dear Students,

Here at Manhattan Review, we constantly strive to provide you the best educational content for standardized test preparation. We make a tremendous effort to keep making things better and better for you. This is especially important with respect to an examination such as the GRE: the typical GRE aspirant is confused with so many test-prep options available. Your challenge is to choose a book or a tutor that prepares you for attaining your goal. We cannot say that we are one of the best; it is you who has to be the judge of that.

There are umpteen numbers of books on Quantitative Reasoning on GRE preparation. What is so different about this book? The answer lies in its approach to deal with the questions. The book is meant to develop you fundamentals. It does not have problems on the GRE's four question types. The purpose of the book is to sharpen your math fundamentals. We have tried our best to cover all the possible concepts in GRE math.

The concepts are explained with the help of text-cum-graphic aid. It is a treat to read the book along with relevant graphics; pictures speak louder than words!

Few short-cut techniques such as 'See-Saw technique' and 'Some Application of Percent and fraction' on the topic of Fraction and Percent are copyright treat for the students. We believe that you will save your precious time in solving the questions at ease.

The Manhattan Review's 'Fundamentals of GRE math' book is holistic and comprehensive in all respects. Should you have any queries, please feel free to write to me at info@review.in.

Happy Learning!

Dr. Joern Meissner

Chapter 2

The GRE Test

2.1 The GRE Revised General Test

The GRE score is one of the most important factors in graduate school admissions. The importance placed upon GRE scores varies widely among schools and even among departments within schools. Its importance can vary from being a formality to being an important selection criterion.

In August 2011, the GRE has undergone significant changes. The revised General GRE test is not adaptive on a question-to-question basis, but is adaptive on section-to-section basis. Your performance on any section— Verbal or Quants— determines the difficulty level of subsequent sections. Though the overhauled test maintained many of the question types from its old version, the scoring scale was revised to a new 130-170 scale from the old 200-800 scale.

2.2 Test Design

The revised section-to-section adaptive test lets you skip questions and come back to them later within a section. Salient features are:

(1) Skip questions, and come back to them later within a section—"Mark and Review" features to tag questions

You can view all the questions from the "Review List", and even attempt any question in any order; however we do not advise this practice. You must attempt questions as they come, and you can mark 2/3 questions later if you wish to come back to them if time permits; however it seldom happens as you would not have much time left at the end of the last question of the section.

Practice the following in a section.

(a) Attempt questions as they come

   (b) If you come across a difficult question, do click the option as per your best guess and "mark" it so that you may come back to it if time permits

   (c) Once you have attempted the last question or you are left with 30 seconds, click "Review List" to see if you have skipped a question unmarked or you wish to quickly revisit a "marked to review" question

(2) Total of five optional breaks (Four 1-minute breaks and one 10-minute break)

(3) Basic on-screen calculator for the Quantitative Reasoning section

To experience the new computer-adaptive test, you should download ETS' POWERPREP II software.

2.3   The New Adaptive Algorithm

The old GRE test adapted within each section on a question-to-question basis. The old GRE algorithm would present you with a medium difficulty level question. If the test taker answered a few questions correctly, questions would become gradually difficult; however if the test taker answered the questions incorrectly, questions would become easier.

The revised GRE test adapts only between sections. Since the revised GRE has two sections for math, two sections for verbal, and an experimental section (either Verbal or Quants), the test would adapt four times.

The level of difficulty of questions in sections is random. There is no order of difficulty on the revised GRE. Easier and harder questions would appear in any order in the test. This implies that each question is weighted the same.

2.4   Scaled score percentiles

The percentiles for the revised General GRE test and its equivalent old GRE percentiles are as follows.

	Verbal Reasoning		Quantitative Reasoning	
Scaled score	Percentile	Old scaled score	Percentile	Old scaled score
170	99	760–800	98	800
169	99	740–750	97	800
168	98	720–730	96	800
167	97	710	95	800
166	96	700	93	800
165	95	680–690	91	790
164	93	660–670	89	790
163	91	650	87	780
162	89	630–640	84	770
161	87	620	81	770
160	84	600–610	78	760
159	81	590	75	750
158	78	570–580	72	740
157	73	560	69	730
156	70	540–550	65	720
155	66	530	61	700–710
154	62	510–520	57	690
153	58	500	53	680
152	53	480–490	49	660–670
151	49	460–470	45	640–650
150	44	450	41	630
149	40	430–440	37	610–620
148	36	420	33	590–600
147	32	410	29	570–580
146	28	390–400	25	550–560
145	24	380	22	530–540
144	21	370	18	500–520
143	18	350–360	15	480–490
142	15	340	13	460–470
141	12	330	11	430–450
140	10	320	8	400–420
139	7	310	6	380–390
138	6	300	5	350–370
137	5	290	3	330–340
136	3	280	2	300–320
135	2	280	2	280–290

134	2	270	1	260–270
133	1	260	1	240–250
132	1	250	<1	220–230
131	1	240	<1	200–210
130	<1	200–230	<1	200

2.5   Analytical Writing score percentiles

Analytical Writing score	Percentile
6	99
5.5	97
5	93
4.5	78
4	54
3.5	35
3	14
2.5	6
2	2
1.5	1
1	<1
0.5	<1

2.6   GRE for Admission to Business Schools

A growing number of MBA programs now accept GRE General Test scores instead of the GMAT. In fact, more than 700 MBA programs now accept GRE General Test scores. As more and more undergrad students are interested in business school, business schools wish to have choices from diversified pool of students, and not only pool of students with a background in business management.

2.7   Difference between the GRE and the GMAT

Here is a comprehensive table which compares the two tests on many parameters.

	GRE	GMAT

Why Take It	GRE score is required for admission to most graduate schools and a growing number of business schools

The GRE General Test is available at more than 850 test centers in more than 160 countries | GMAT score is required for admission to most business schools, but it is not eligible for admission to graduate schools

The GMAT Test is available at more than 600 test centers in more than 114 countries |
| **How many take the test?** | Over 650,000 per year | Over 250,000 per year |
| **Test Structure** | • A 60-minute Analytical Writing section with two essays

• Two 30-minute each Verbal Reasoning sections

• Two 35-minute each Quantitative Reasoning sections

Verbal or Quantitative sections can come in any order.

• A 30 or 35-minute un-scored, unidentified section that can be either Quant or Verbal

• There may a last, un-scored and identified "Research section" | • A 30-minute Analytical section with one essay, and a 30-minute Integrated Reasoning section

• A 75-minute Quantitative section

• A 75- minute Verbal section |

Test Format	• Paper-based • Computer-adaptive Section adaptive: GRE computer-adaptive test is NOT adaptive within sections (NOT adaptive on a question-by-question basis); it is adaptive between sections. Within a section, you can skip questions and go back to attempt them if time permits.	• Only computer-adaptive format Question adaptive: GMAT computer-adaptive test is adaptive within sections (adaptive on a question-by-question basis); it is NOT adaptive between sections. You cannot skip questions, hence there is no question of going back to attempt them.
Test Dates	• Throughout the year (You can take the computer-adaptive Test once every 21 days, up to five times within any 365 days) • Paper-based tests are administered up to three times a year	• Throughout the year (You can take the computer-adaptive Test once every 31 days, up to five times within any 365 days)
How It's Scored	• Verbal and Quantitative score ranges from 130 to 170 in 1-point increments • Analytical Writing is scored on a scale of 0-6 Official scores are reported within 20-21 days from the test date. You can view unofficial Verbal and Quant scores upon submitting the test.	• The overall, or composite, GMAT score ranges from 200 to 800 in 10-point increments • Analytical Writing is scored on a scale of 0-6 • Integrated Reasoning (IR) is scored on a scale of 1-8 Official scores are reported within 20-21 days from the test date. You can view unofficial Verbal, Quant, and IR scores upon submitting the test.

Fee **Rescheduling** **Addl. Score** **card** **Cancellation** **refund**	$195 (Apply to four programs for free) $50 $27 $97.50 (If cancelled no later than 4 days before the exam)	$250 (Apply to five programs for free) $50 $28 $80 (If cancelled no later than 4 days before the exam)
Testing Time	3 hours 45 minutes plus short breaks	3 hours 30 minutes plus short breaks
How Long Are Scores Valid For?	5 years	5 years
Content	**Analytical Writing**	**Analytical Writing Task (AWA) &** **Integrated Reasoning (IR)**
	• Essay on an issue (30 minutes) • Essay on an argument (30 minutes)	• Essay on an argument (30 minutes) • Integrated Reasoning (IR) (12 questions; 30 minutes)
Content	**Verbal Reasoning** **(Computer-adaptive test: Approx. 20 questions; 2 sections; 30 minutes per section)** **Paper-based test will have Approx. 25 questions**	**Verbal Ability** **(41 questions; 75 minutes)**
	• Sentence Equivalence • Text Completion (Content-wise both Sentence Equivalence & Text Completion are similar. Vocabulary is tested in these types of questions, which makes the GRE different from the GMAT.) • Reading Comprehension (Critical Reasoning is not a separate part, it is tested within Reading Comprehension)	• Sentence Correction (Emphasis is on grammar and sentence construction and not on vocabulary) • Reading Comprehension • Critical Reasoning (More number of CR questions asked in the GMAT than are in the GRE; more complex arguments)
Question types/ Formats	**Verbal Reasoning**	**Verbal Ability**

	• Multiple choice (Only one option correct out of five options) • Multiple answers (More than one option is correct; select all the correct options) • Select a sentence in the passage There would be two scored sections and may be one un-scored experimental section	• Multiple choice (Only one option correct out of five options) There would be only one section
Content	**Quantitative Reasoning** **(Computer-adaptive test: 20 questions; 2 sections; 35 minutes per section)** **Paper-based test will have 25 questions**	**Quantitative Ability** **(37 questions; 75 minutes)**
	• Arithmetic • Algebra • Geometry • Word Problems • Data Interpretation GRE math is relatively easier than GMAT math. GRE math emphasizes more on Geometry, Arithmetic and Data Interpretation.	• Arithmetic • Algebra • Geometry • Word Problems • Data Interpretation GMAT verbal is relatively easier than GRE verbal. (No vocabulary in the GMAT) GMAT math emphasizes more on Number properties and Sets.
Question types/ Formats	**Quantitative Reasoning**	**Quantitative Ability**

• **Multiple choice** (Only one option correct out of five options) • **Multiple answers** (More than one option is correct; select all the correct options) • **Numeric Entry** (Type the answer) • **Quantitative Comparison** (Compare two quantities, and select one correct option out of four options) Basic calculator is available in GRE Quants section; however it is not advisable to use the calculator frequently! There would be two scored sections and may be one unscored section	• **Multiple choice** (Only one option correct out of five options; there are two question formats: Problem Solving and Data Sufficiency) Calculator is NOT available in GMAT Quants section; however it is available in Integrated Reasoning section. There would be only one section

2.8 Which test is right for me—GRE or GMAT?

Which test is better for you— the GMAT or the GRE—should be judged by you. Appear for a couple of mock tests of both the tests and then decide. We offer free full-length computer-adaptive diagnostic tests for both the tests.

Though GMAT and GRE scores are incomparable as both the tests are unique, ETS (Administrator of the GRE) and GMAC (Administrator of the GMAT) have devised their comparison metrics to put scores in each other's perspective. Comparison chart for the GRE to the GMAT is available on the ETS site.

2.9   Structure of the test

Section #	Section	Time
1	Essay on an issue	30 minutes
	Essay on an argument	30 minutes
	Optional 1 minute break	
2	Verbal Reasoning or Quantitative Reasoning*	30 minutes (VR); 35 minutes (QR)
	Optional 1 minute break	
3	Verbal Reasoning or Quantitative Reasoning*	30 minutes (VR); 35 minutes (QR)
	Optional 10 minutes break	
4	Verbal Reasoning or Quantitative Reasoning*	30 minutes (VR); 35 minutes (QR)
	Optional 1 minute break	
5	Verbal Reasoning or Quantitative Reasoning*	30 minutes (VR); 35 minutes (QR)
	Optional 1 minute break	
6 (Not necessarily last section; may appear in any order)	Verbal Reasoning or Quantitative Reasoning* *Any of of the sections from 2 to 6 would be an experimental and would be un-scored; there would be at least two Verbal Reasoning or Quantitative Reasoning sections	30 minutes (VR); 35 minutes (QR)
Last section	Research section *There may be a variable, identified, but unsecured section	Normally 12 questions in 3o minutes

We can help you prepare for the GRE with high score. You can join our tutoring classes or buy books to study by yourself. We recommend that you to attempt a free diagnostic test to assess yourself.

Chapter 3

GRE— Quantitative Reasoning

Quantitative Reasoning section of the GRE exam tests your skill on two types of questions based on quantitative aptitude or loosely speaking mathematical proficiency.

Quantitative Reasoning assesses your basic mathematical skills, understanding of elementary mathematical concepts up to the secondary or the high school level, ability to reason quantitatively and to frame and solve problems with quantitative approaches. You will not be asked questions based on higher level mathematics.

As you are aware that there would be two scored and may be one un-scored, experimental section on the test day. Computer-delivered test would have 20 questions per section to be attempted in 35 minutes. So you have to see at least 40 math questions on the test day. If there is an experimental section, you may see 60 quants questions.

The GRE frames questions based on the concepts of Arithmetic, Elementary Algebra, Word Problems, Elementary Geometry, Co-ordinate Geometry, Elementary Statistics, Functions, and Data Interpretation.

The scope of the book is to introduce you to elementary mathematics required to do well in the GRE. We have not discussed question types and format that GRE use in the test. Separate, topic-wise books will cover the scope of GRE questions.

Following topics are included in the GRE questions:

Arithmetic:

- Numbers, their classification, and application
    - Properties of Integers, Even & Odd numbers, Prime numbers, Decimals, and Fractions
    - Factors and Multiplicands
    - LCM and HCF (GCD)
    - Divisibility Rules

- Mathematical operations

- PEMDAS

- Exponents (Powers), and Surds

- Ratio and Proportion

- Percents

- Simple and Compound Interest

- Profit and Loss

- Time and Distance

- Work and Rate

- Mixtures and Alligation

- Mensuration (Measurement calculation)

- Counting Methods: Permutation and Combination

- Discrete Probability

Algebra:

- Algebraic Expressions

- Linear equations: Solving system of Linear equation

- Quadratic equations: Solving Quadratic equations

- Functions

- Absolute numbers

- Inequalities

Geometry:

- Lines

- Circles

- Polygons: Triangles, Quadrilaterals

- Solids: Cube, Cuboid, Cylinder, Sphere, and Cone

- Mensuration (Measurement calculation)

- Co-ordinate Geometry

Statistics:

- Average: Mean, Median, and Mode

- Data Interpretation

Following questions types are asked in the test.

• Multiple choice (Only one option correct out of five options)

• Multiple answers (More than one options are correct; select all the correct options)

• Numeric Entry (Type the answer in a rectangle box)

• Quantitative Comparison (Compare two quantities, and select one correct option out of four options)

Basic calculator is available in GRE Quants section; however it is not advisable to use the calculator frequently!

3.1 Understanding numbers

Numbers—the backbone of GRE quants; we all are familiar with numbers, but the devil lies in detail!

Let us understand the numbers from the GRE perspective.

3.1.1 Classification of numbers

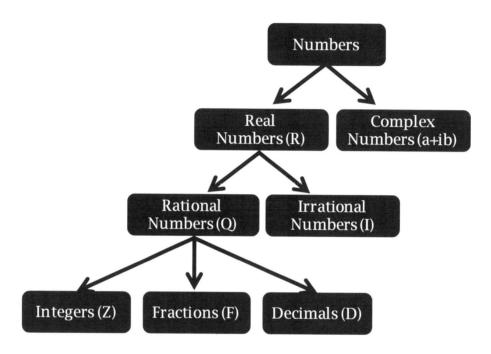

(A) **Real numbers:** Almost all the numbers you can imagine are Real numbers. Any number that can be represented on a number line is a real number. These include $0, 1, -3, 4/3, -0.3457, 48.87, \sqrt{3}, \pi$, and many more!

If most numbers are real numbers, then what are not real numbers?

The numbers such as $\sqrt{-1}, (2 + \sqrt{-5})$etc. are not real numbers. They are Imaginary number and Complex numbers respectively.

Real numbers can further be classified into Rational and Irrational numbers.

(a) **Rational numbers:** Numbers that can be expressed in the form of $\dfrac{p}{q}$ where p and q are integers, and $q \neq 0$. Remember that p may be 0.

The above definition may look a little scary to those who are not very familiar with the concepts of numbers; however the good news for them is that you need not know the above definition to master the GRE quants.

So what do rational numbers include? Simply put, these include all **integers, decimal, and fractions.**

So what do rational numbers exclude? These exclude roots of non-perfect square numbers, roots of non-perfect cube numbers, special numbers such as $\pi = 3.14, e = 2.718$, and many others.

Rational numbers can be broadly classified into three categories—Integers, Fractions, and Decimals.

i. **Integers:** All counting numbers are integers whether negative, positive or zero.
   Example: {1,2,3,4,5,...} are called positive integers; {-1,-2,-3,-4,-5,....} are called negative integers. Note that "0" is also an integer.

   In Data Sufficiency questions, you may come across terms like non-negative integers or non-positive integers. A non-negative integer would be one among the set of {0,1,2,3,4,5,...}; note that "0" is included; whereas a non-positive integer would be one among the set of {0,-1,-2,-3,-4,-5,...}.

ii. **Fractions:** Any number that can be expressed with a numerator and a denominator is called fraction. In other words, a number that can be expressed in the form of x/y is a fraction such that $y \neq 0$. **Example:** 1/3, 5/4, -3/8 etc.

iii. **Decimal numbers:** Decimal numbers are another way of expressing fractions. The decimal numbers are written with the use of a decimal ("."). The left of the decimal point (.) has place values of digits for units, tens, hundreds, thousands, and more; whereas the right of the decimal point (.) has place values of digits for tenths, hundredths, thousandths, and more.

   We will discuss place value in the following pages.

(b) **Irrational numbers:** Numbers that cannot be expressed in the form of $\dfrac{p}{q}$ where p and q are integers, and $q \neq 0$ are irrational numbers or in other words, all real numbers that are not rational are irrational numbers. These include roots of non-perfect squared numbers: 2,5,and others; roots of non-perfect cube numbers, special numbers such as $\pi = 3.14, e = 2.718$, and many others.

By default any number mentioned in the QA section is a **real number**; so, you must NOT assume that it is an integer until stated as such.

3.1.2 Number line

A number line is a line with "0" as its center. Numbers on the right side of "0" are positive and those on the left side are negative. Number line helps define the direction of measurement.

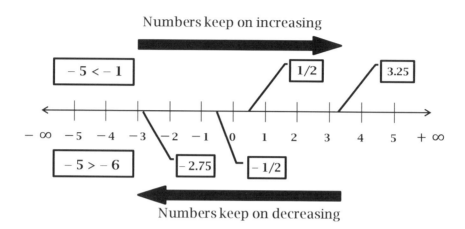

3.1.3 Basic operations on numbers

Symbol	Mathematical operation	Application	Examples
+	Addition	Sum, Add, Plus, Total, Increase	$2 + 3 = 5$; (Two positives will be added) $(-2) + (-3) = -5$; (Two negatives will be added) $2 + (-3) = -1$; (A positive and a negative will be subtracted) $(-2) + 3 = 1$; (A negative and a positive will be subtracted)
−	Subtraction	Deduct, Minus, Decrease, Less, Reduce, Difference	$2 - 3 = -1$; (Two positives will be subtracted) $(-2) - (-3) = 1$; (Two negatives will be subtracted) $2 - (-3) = 5$; (A positive and a negative will be added) $(-2) - 3 = -5$; (A negative and a positive will be added)
×	Multiplication	Multiply, Product, Times, ×, By, Increase	$2 \times 3 = 6$; (Positive × Positive = Positive) $(-2) \times (-3) = 6$; (Negative × Negative = Positive) $2 \times (-3) = -6$; (Positive × Negative = Negative) $(-2) \times 3 = -6$; (Negative × Positive = Negative)

÷	Division	Divide, Quotient, Part of, Per unit calculation	$6 \div 3 = 2$; (Positive ÷ Positive = Positive)
			$(-6) \div (-3) = 2$; (Negative ÷ Negative = Positive)
			$6 \div (-3) = -2$; (Positive ÷ Negative = Negative)
			$(-6) \div 3 = -2$; (Negative ÷ Positive = Negative)

3.1.4   Face value and place value

The number system we use is set up from ten symbols only $\{0, 1, 2, 3, 4, 5, 6, 7, 8, 9\}$. Each symbol is called a digit and each has its value called **Face value.** So, the face value of "9" is nine times the face value of the digit "1" or three times the face value of the digit "3". For example, for numbers 243, & 234, the face values of digits "2", "3", and "4" do not vary upon their placement.

Place value of a digit varies depending on where it is placed in a number. For example, for numbers 234, and 243, the place values of digits "3", and "4" are different.

If a digit placed on the left of a digit, its place value becomes 10 times. For a number 234, the place value of digit "2" is 200, that of digit "3" is 30, and that of "4" is 4. Similarly, the place values of digits placed after the decimal point ($\cdot$) reduces in its value by 1/10 times. This can be better understood this way.

$$243 = 2 \times 100 + 4 \times 10 + 3 \times 1;$$

$$234 = 2 \times 100 + 3 \times 10 + 4 \times 1.$$

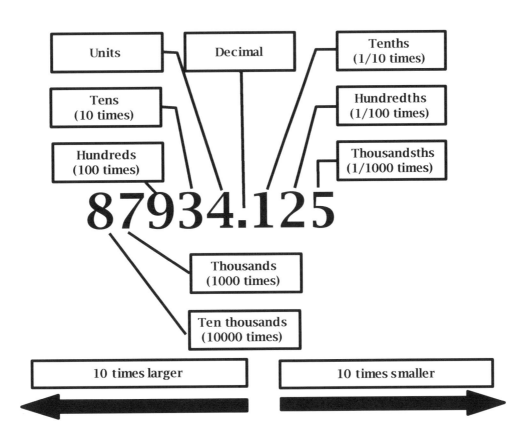

3.1.5 Even and Odd numbers

Even number: An integer completely divisible by "2" and does not leave a remainder is called an **Even number.** In other words, an even number can be expressed as "$2m$", where "m" is an integer. As per this definition, "0" is an even integer. **Example:** {0, 2, 4, 6, 8,...}

Odd number: An integer when divided by "2" leaves a remainder "1" is called **Odd number.** In other words, an odd number can be expressed as $(2m + 1)$, where "m" is an integer. All the integers are either even or odd integers. **Example:** {1, 3, 5, 7,...}

Basic operations on Even and Odd numbers:

Mathematical operation	Application	Examples
Addition/ Subtraction	Even + Even = Even; Odd + Odd = Even; Even + Odd = Odd Any number of even numbers can make an even number; however only an even number of odd numbers can make an even number; e.g.: Two odd numbers on addition gives even, four odd numbers on addition also gives even.	4 + 2 = 6; 4 − 2 = 2; Even 7 + 3 = 10; 7 − 3 = 4; Even 5 + 2 = 7; 5 − 2 = 3; Odd
Multiplication	Even × Even = Even; Odd×Odd = Odd; Even×Odd = Even Multiplication of any number of odd numbers always results in another odd number.	4×2 = 8; Even 3×3 = 9; Odd 2×3 = 6; Even

	If the product of two integers is Even and one of them is an Even integer, we cannot comment on the nature of the other number, i.e. whether it is Even or Odd.	
Division	Not every operation of Division is completely divisible. We show you the results if the division leaves no remainder. Odd ÷ Odd = Odd; Even ÷ Odd = Even; Odd ÷ Even = Not divisible; Even ÷ Even = Even or Odd	$9 \div 3 = 3$; Odd $10 \div 5 = 2$; Even $11 \div 2 =?$ Not divisible $4 \div 2 = 2$; Even $10 \div 2 = 5$; Odd

3.1.6 Consecutive numbers

An ordered set of continuous integers written in ascending order are called **Consecutive numbers.**

Example: $\{23, 24, 25\}, \{-2, -1, 0, 1, 2, 3\}$

Example of consecutive Even numbers: $\{12, 14, 16\}$;

Example of consecutive Odd numbers: $\{11, 13, 15\}$

3.1.7 Prime numbers

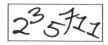 A number greater than "1" which has no factors other than "1" and the number itself, is called **Prime number.** In other words, a number ONLY divisible by "1" and itself is called Prime number.

Example: $\{2, 3, 5, 7, 11, 13, 17, 23, 29, ...\}$ There are infinitely many Prime numbers.

First 25 prime numbers are:

$\{2, 3, 5, 7, 11, 13, 17, 23, 29, 31, 37, 41, 43, 47, 53, 59, 61, 67, 71, 73, 79, 83, 89, 97\}$ 101

"2" is the only even prime number or all the prime numbers are odd except "2".

How to verify whether a number "n" is a prime number:

Step1: Take square root of the number; if square root is an integer the number is not prime number, else follow the next step.

Step2: Say the largest integer closest to the square root of the number "n" is "m"; where $m < \sqrt{n}$;

Step3: Divide "n" by all the prime numbers from "2 to m", inclusive, if n is divisible by any number among them, then the number "n" is not prime, else prime

=> Let us take a number "$n = 101$".

Step1: $10 < \sqrt{101} < 11$; not an integer;

Step2: $\sqrt{101} = \approx 10 = m$;

Step3: Divide 101 by prime numbers from 2 to 10 i.e. 2, 3, 5, & 7. Since 101 is not divisible by any prime number among these, hence 101 is a prime number.

=> Let us take a number "$n = 87$".

Step1: $9 < \sqrt{87}, 10$; not an integer;

Step2: $\sqrt{87} = \approx 9 = m$;

Step3: Divide 87 by prime numbers from 2 to 9 i.e. 2, 3, 5, & 7. Since 87 is divisible by 3, hence 87 is not a prime number

3.1.8 Co-Prime numbers

Two numbers are co-prime to each other if they have no factor common between them except '1'.

Example: 14 & 15. The factors of "14" are {1, 2, 7, 14}, and the factors of "15" are {1, 3, 5, 15}. There is no factor common between "14 & 15" except '1', so "14 & 15" are co-prime to each other.

It is important to know that the LCM of co-prime numbers is their product, and GCD or HCF is "1". Say two numbers "a" and "b" are co-prime to each other, then **LCM** = $a \times b$, and **GCD = 1**.

LCM = least common multiple

GCD = greatest common divisor

HCF = highest common factor   ex. common factors 12 & 18 are
1, 2, 3, ⑥ HCF = 6

3.1.9 Rounding off

Rounding off a number means to get a significant and practically usable number. Say, if I say that Manhattan to JFK airport is 15.24 miles, we can truncate the hundredth place digit to get a number which is rounded off to tenth place equalling 15.2 miles; however by doing this, we do get a less accurate number. The degree of rounding off a number depends on how much accurate number you want. In this case, even the additional 0.2 miles may seem insignificant to a regular commuter. So, 15.2 can further be rounded off to the nearest tens as 15 miles which is further less accurate.

Steps to round off numbers:

Step 1: Keep a tab on the digit you wish to keep.

Step 2: Drop the right-most digit of the number.

  A. If the dropped digit is more than '5', increase the digit you wish to keep (i.e. the digit to the left of the dropped digit) by '1'. However, if the dropped digit is less than '5', then leave the digit you wish to keep as it is. If the dropped digit is equal to '5', then there are two scenarios:

   (a) If the digit before the dropped digit is even, keep it unchanged.

   (b) If the digit before the dropped digit is odd, increase it by 1.

Step 3: Repeat the above steps for the number derived in step 2.A, till you get the desired number mentioned in step 1.

Example: Rounding off 15.8454 to nearest tenth.

Step 1: Say, we wish to keep the number till nearest tenth. The number would be 15.8.

Step 2: 15.8454: The right-most digit is "4".

Number achieved = 15.845 as the right-most digit (4) is not "5" or more than "5".

Step 3: 15.845: The right-most digit is "5".

Number achieved = 15.84 as the right-most digit is "5" and the previous digit is even (4).

Step 4: 15.84: The right-most digit is "4".

Number achieved = 15.8 as the right-most digit is "4".

Note that the number, rounded off, can be more than or less than the original number. 15.8454 rounded off to 15.8 < 15.8454 whereas another number 15.8554 rounded off to 15.9 > 15.8554.

3.1.10   Order of operations – PEMDAS

Please Excuse My Dear Aunt Sally

12 ÷ 2(1+2)?

2 or 18

What is the value of $2\{32 - 2(6 \times 5^2 - 50 + 25 \div 5)\}$?

$(6 \times 25 - 50 + 25 \div 5)$
$(150 - 50 + 25 \div 5)$
$150 - 50 + 5)$
$(150 - 55$
$2\{32 - 2(95)\}$
$(32 - 190)$
$2(-158)$
-316

Follow the order of operation given as below:

P: Parentheses first

E: Exponents (i.e. Powers and Square Roots, etc.)

MD: Multiplication and Division (left-to-right)

AS: Addition and Subtraction (left-to-right)

Expression	Comments
$2\{10^2 - 2(6 \times 5^2 - 50 + 25 \div 5)\}$ 100 25	Solve the parenthesis first. If there are more than two parentheses, follow the order: [ ], { }, & ( ). Here, we will solve { } first, and then ( ). **(P)**
$= 2\{\mathbf{100} - 2(6 \times \mathbf{25} - 50 \div 25)\}$	Among the operators exponent, multiplication, division, addition, subtraction, solve the exponent first. **(E)**
$= 2\{100 - 2(\mathbf{150} - 50 + 5)\}$	Multiplication and division can be done simultaneously. **(MD)**
$= 2\{100 - 2(\mathbf{105})\}$ $= 2\{100 - \mathbf{210}\}$ $= 2\{-110\}$ $= -220$	Addition and subtraction can be done simultaneously. **(AS)**

3.1.11 Divisibility

A number is said to be divisible by another number if the division does not leave any remainder. Following are quick reckoner rules for divisibility test.

Divisor	Condition: A number is divisible	Example
2	if the unit digit is Even: {0, 2, 4, 6, 8}	268; 126596
3	if the Sum of all the digits is divisible by "3"	21681; Sum of digits = 2+1+6+8+1 = 18; 18 div. by 3 implies that 21681 is divisible by 3.

89896; Sum of digits = 8+9+8+9+6 = 40; 40 not div. by 3 implies that 89896 is not divisible by 3. |
| 4 | if the number formed out of last two digits are divisible by "4" | 1224 and 2356 are div. by 4 as 24 and 56 are divisible by 4.

1254 and 2569866 are not div. by 4 as 54 and 66 are not divisible by 4. |
| 5 | if the unit digit is "0" or "5". | 1220 and 2355 are div. by 5.

1254 and 2569866 are not div. by 5. |
| 6 | if the number is divisible by both "2" and "3"; follow the divisibility rules of "2" and "3". | 1254, and 89892 are div. by 6. |
| 8 | if the number formed out of the last three digits are divisible by "8" | 891224 and 2542352 are div. by 8.

561354 and 2569866 are not div. by 8. |

9	if the Sum of all digits of the number is divisible by "9"	21681; Sum of digits = 2+1+6+8+1=18; 18 div. by 9 implies that 21681 is divisible by 9. 89896; Sum of digits = 8+9+8+9+6 = 40; 40 not div. by 9 implies that 89896 is not divisible by 9.
10	if the unit digit is "0".	12340 and 5245870.
11	if the difference of the sum of digits at odd places, and that at even places is either "0" or divisible by "11".	251384; S.O. = Sum of digits at odd places = 4+3+5 = 11; S.E. = Sum of digits at even places = 8+1+2 = 11; S.O.– S.E. = 11–11 = **0** implies that 251384 is div. by 11. 81927092; S.O. – S.E. = 5 – 27 = – **22** div. by 11 implies that 81927092 is div. by 11.

3.1.12 Factors

All the possible divisors of an integer which leave no reminder are called factors.
Example: The factors of '6' are 1, 2, 3, & 6. We can write 6 as 1×6 or 2×3.

Factors of 60:

$$60 = 1 \times 60;$$
$$= 2 \times 30;$$
$$= 3 \times 20;$$
$$= 4 \times 15;$$
$$= 5 \times 12;$$
$$= 6 \times 10.$$

So, the factors of '60' are $\{1, 2, 3, 4, 5, 6, 10, 12, 15, 20, 30, 60\}$. Remember that '1' and the number itself are also the factors of a number.

Number of factors

Say, a number N can be written as $N = a^x b^y c^z$, where a, b, and c are prime factors of the number N, and x, y, and z are positive integers, then

=> **Number of factors** (including '1' and the number itself) = $(x + 1)(y + 1)(z + 1)$;

=> **Number of factors** (excluding '1' and the number itself) = $(x + 1)(y + 1)(z + 1) - 2$.

Number of factors of 24:

$24 = 2 \times 2 \times 2 \times 3 = 2^3 \times 3^1$; here $a = 2$, & $b = 3$ are prime numbers, and $x = 2$, & $y = 1$.

Hence the number of factors of 24 including '1' and the number itself = $(3 + 1)(1 + 1) = 4.2 = 8$.

Let us verify this.

Factors of 24 are: $\{1, 2, 3, 4, 6, 8, 12, 28\}$; total number of factors equals to 8.

Let us take one more example.

Number of factors of 2520:

$2520 = 2 \times 2 \times 2 \times 3 \times 3 \times 5 \times 7 = 2^3 \times 3^2 \times 5 \times 7$; here $2, 3, 5$, & 7 are prime numbers.

Hence the number of factors of 2520 including '1' and the number itself = $(3 + 1)(2 + 1)(1 + 1)(1 + 1) = 4.3.2.2 = 48$.

Sum of all the factors:

Say, a number N can be written as $N = a^x b^y c^z$, where a, b, and c are prime factors of number N, x, y, and z are positive integers, then

=> **Sum of all the factors** (including 1 and the number itself) = $\left[\dfrac{a^{x+1} - 1}{a - 1}\right]\left[\dfrac{b^{y+1} - 1}{b - 1}\right]\left[\dfrac{c^{z+1} - 1}{c - 1}\right]$

Sum of all the factors of 60:

$60 = 2^2 . 3^1 . 5^1$;

Sum of all the factors (including 1 and the number itself) = $\left[\dfrac{2^{2+1} - 1}{2 - 1}\right]\left[\dfrac{3^{1+1} - 1}{3 - 1}\right]\left[\dfrac{5^{1+1} - 1}{5 - 1}\right]$

$= 7.(8/2).(24/4) = 168.$

Let us cross check this. Sum of all the factors of $60 = 1 + 2 + 3 + 4 + 5 + 6 + 10 + 12 + 15 + 20 + 30 + 60 = 168$.

3.1.13 Perfect Square numbers

A perfect square number is a non-negative integer that can be expressed as the product of an integer with itself. In other words, a number which is a square of any integer is called Perfect square number. Perfect square numbers are always non-negative integers.

Example: $\{0, 1, 4, 9, 16, 25, 36, 49, ...\}$. Some mathematicians do not consider that "0" is a perfect square number. Moreover the GRE does not assume that you know the meaning of "perfect square number." The phrase used typically is "square of an integer."

We can see that $1 = 1 \times 1 = -1 \times -1$; and $4 = 2 \times 2 = -2 \times -2$.

Some properties of perfect square:
- The number of distinct factors of a perfect square number is ALWAYS Odd.
- The sum of distinct factors of a perfect square number is ALWAYS Odd.
- A perfect square number ALWAYS has an Odd number of Odd-factors, and Even number of Even-factors.
- Perfect square number ALWAYS has even number of powers of prime factors.

3.1.14 Multiples

While the factors divide the number completely, multiples are divisible by the number itself completely.

Example: The factors of '6' are 1,2,3 & 6; and the multiples of '6' are 6,12,18,24,30,...

=> A number is both a factor and a multiple of itself.

=> There are a finite number of factors of a number, but there are an infinite number of multiples.

In other words, we can write that the **multiples of a number $N = k.N$,** where k is a positive integer. So the multiples of a number, say, xy^2 would be $xy^2, 2xy^2, 3xy^2, 4xy^2, ...$ and the factors of xy^2 would be $\{1, x, xy, y^2, xy^2\}$.

3.1.15 Lowest Common Multiple—LCM

We all know what the LCM is; but occasionally we may get confused with HCF. Let us understand LCM.

The LCM has three properties:

(1) It is a **multiple;** for numbers 6 & 10, the multiples of 6 are $\{6, 12, 18, 24, 30, 36, 42, 48, 54, 60, ...$ and the multiples of 10 are $\{10, 20, 30, 40, 50, 60, 70, 80, 90, ...\}$, so LCM is one among these multiples.

(2) It is a **common multiple** among all the multiples of 6, & 10; for numbers 6 & 10, the common multiples are $\{30, 60, 90, ...\}$, so it is one among these multiples.

(3) It is the **least common multiple (LCM)** among all the common multiples; for numbers 6 & 10, the least common multiple is **30: LCM.**

So, in other words, LCM of numbers is the smallest possible number which gets divided by each number without leaving any reminder.

Did you notice that in math, we never come across a term—Highest Common Multiple? It is because it is insignificant to discuss this as the Highest Common Multiple for any set of numbers would always be infinite; multiples of numbers are never ending.

Computation of LCM by factor method:

Example: Computation of LCM of 24, 54, and 70:

Step1: Factorise the numbers into prime factors

=> $24 = 2^3.3$;
=> $54 = 2.3^3$;

=> $70 = 2.\mathbf{5.7}$

Step2: Select the term with the highest exponent for each prime factor

=> The prime factors with their highest exponents are $2^3, 3^3, 5, \& 7$.

Step3: Multiply the numbers selected in step 2; it is the LCM of numbers.

=> **LCM** = $2^3.3^3.5.7 =$ **7560.**

Computation of LCM of algebraic expressions:

Example: Computation of LCM of $10xy^2z^5, 15x^2y^3z^4, \& 24x^3y^3z$:

=> $10xy^2z^5 = 2.\mathbf{5}.x.y^2.\mathbf{z^5}$;
=> $15x^2y^3z^4 = 3.5.x^2.\mathbf{y^3}.x^4$;
=> $24x^3y^3z = \mathbf{2^3}.3.\mathbf{x^3}.y^3.z$

LCM of $10xy^2z^5, 15x^2y^3z^4, \& 24x^3y^3z = 2^3.3.5.x^3.y^3.z^5 = \mathbf{120x^3y^3z^5}$

3.1.16   Highest Common Factor—HCF OR Greatest Common Divisor—GCD

Let us understand HCF.

Like LCM, the HCF/GCD also has three properties:

(1) It is a **factor**; for numbers 18 & 24, the factors of 6 are $\{1, 2, 3, 6, 9, 18\}$, and the factors of 24 are $\{1, 2, 3, 4, 6, 8, 12, 24\}$, so HCF is one among these factors.

(2) It is a **common factor** among these factors; for numbers 18 & 24, the common factors are $\{1, 2, 3, 6\}$, so it is one among these factors.

(3) It is the **highest common factor (HCF)** among all the factors; for numbers 18 & 24, the highest common factor is **6: HCF**.

So, in other words, HCF of numbers is the largest possible number which divides each number without leaving any reminder.

Did you notice that in math, we never come across a term—Lowest Common Factor? It is because it is insignificant to discuss this as the Lowest Common Factor for any set of numbers would always be '1'.

Computation of HCF by factor method:

Example: Computation of HCF of 24, 54, and 210.

Step1: Factorise the numbers into prime factors

$$\Rightarrow 24 = 2^3.3;$$
$$\Rightarrow 54 = 2.3^3;$$
$$\Rightarrow 210 = 2.3.5.7.$$

Step2: Select the term with the lowest common exponent for each **common** prime factor

$\Rightarrow$ All the common prime factors with their lowest exponents are 2, & 3.

Step3: Multiply the numbers selected in step 2. It is the HCF/GCD of numbers.

$\Rightarrow$ HCF = 2.3 = **6**.

Computation of HCF for algebraic expressions:

Example: Computation of HCF of $10xy^2z^5, 15x^2y^3z^4,$ & $24x^3y^3z$:

$$\Rightarrow 10xy^2z^5 = 2.5.\boldsymbol{x}.\boldsymbol{y}^2.z^5 = 2.5.(\boldsymbol{x}).(\boldsymbol{y}^2).(\boldsymbol{z}).z^4;$$
$$\Rightarrow 15x^2y^3z^4 = 3.5.x^2.y^3.z^4 = 3.5.(\boldsymbol{x}).x.(\boldsymbol{y}^2).y.(\boldsymbol{z}).z^3;$$
$$\Rightarrow 24x^3y^3z = 2^3.3.x^3.y^3.\boldsymbol{z} = 2^3.3.(\boldsymbol{x}).x^2.(\boldsymbol{y}^2).y.(\boldsymbol{z})$$

HCF of $10xy^2z^5, 15x^2y^3z^4,$ & $24x^3y^3z = \boldsymbol{xy^2z}$.

LCM and HCF revisited:

Numbers: N_1, N_2, N_3	LCM of N_1, N_2, N_3 = $\boldsymbol{120x^3y^3z^5}$; LCM gets completely divisible by numbers	HCF of $N_1, N_2, N_3 = \boldsymbol{xy^2z}$; Numbers gets completely divisible by HCF
$N_1 = 10xy^2z^5$	$\dfrac{LCM}{N_1} = \dfrac{120x^3y^3z^5}{10xy^2z^5} = 12x^2y$	$\dfrac{N_1}{HCF} = \dfrac{10xy^2z^5}{xy^2z} = 10z^4$
$N_2 = 15x^2y^3z^4$	$\dfrac{LCM}{N_2} = \dfrac{120x^3y^3z^5}{15x^2y^3z^4} = 8xz$	$\dfrac{N_2}{HCF} = \dfrac{15x^2y^3z^4}{xy^2z} = 15xyz^3$
$N_3 = 24x^3y^3z$	$\dfrac{LCM}{N_3} = \dfrac{120x^3y^3z^5}{24x^3y^3z} = 5z^4$	$\dfrac{N_3}{HCF} = \dfrac{24x^3y^3z}{xy^2z} = 24x^2y^2$

3.2 Exponents

Exponents, also called indices, are powers given to bases. Exponents tell the number of times a number is multiplied by itself.

Example: $2^4 = 2 \times 2 \times 2 \times 2 = 16$. Here '2' is the base and '4' is the exponent or index.

Here are some basic operations of indices:

Operations	Examples
$a^m \times a^n = a^{m+n}$	$2^3 \times 2^5 = 2^{3+5} = 2^8$
$(ab)^m = a^m \times b^m$	$(2 \times 3)^4 = 2^4 \times 3^4$
$a^m \div a^n = a^{m-n}$	$2^3 \div 2^5 = 2^{3-5} = 2^{-2}$
$(a^m)^n = a^{mn}$	$(2^2)^3 = 2^{2.3} = 2^6$
$\dfrac{1}{a^m} = a^{-m}$	$\dfrac{1}{2^3} = 2^{-3}$
$\sqrt[n]{a^m} = (a^m)^{1/n} = a^{m/n}$	$\sqrt[3]{2^6} = (2^6)^{1/3} = 2^{6/3} = 2^2 = 4$
$a^0 = 1$, if $a \neq 0$	$2^0 = 1$
$(-a)^{Even} = +(a)^{Even}, a = $ positive number	$(-2)^4 = -2 \times -2 \times -2 \times -2 = 16$
$(-a)^{Odd} = -(a)^{Odd}, a = $ positive number	$(-2)^3 = -2 \times -2 \times -2 = -8$ or $-(2)^3 = -(2 \times 2 \times 2) = -8$

Note that $(a^m)^n \neq a^{m^n}$

$=> \left(2^2\right)^3 = 2^{2.3} = 2^6 = 64;$

$=> 2^{3^2} = 2^9 = 512 \neq 64.$

$3^2 \cdot 3^4 =$

$3 \cdot 3 \cdot 3 \cdot 3 \cdot 3 \cdot 3 = 3^6$

$\dfrac{3^5}{3^3} = \dfrac{3 \cdot 3 \cdot 3 \cdot 3 \cdot 3}{3 \cdot 3 \cdot 3}$

3^2

$5^{\frac{2}{3}} = \sqrt[3]{5^2} = \sqrt[3]{25}$

$5^{\frac{1}{5}} = \sqrt[5]{5}$

$3 \cdot 5$

$\left(4^2\right)^3 = 2^x$

$\left(\left(2^2\right)^2\right)^3$

$8^{\frac{2}{3}} = \sqrt[3]{8^2} =$

$\left(2^4\right)^3 = 2^{\boxed{12}}$

$\left(\sqrt[3]{8}\right)^2$ $\boxed{3.5}$

$2^2 = 4$

$\left(\dfrac{2}{5}\right)^{-2} = \left(\dfrac{5}{2}\right)^2 = \dfrac{5^2}{2^2} = \dfrac{25}{4}$

$2^{-10} = \dfrac{1}{2^{10}}$

$\left(2^3\right)^4 \neq 2^{\boxed{3^4}}$

2^{12} 2^{81}

3.2.1 Unit digits of numbers with exponents

You may come across a question in which you are asked to deduce the unit digit of a number with a positive integer exponent.

Example: What is the unit digit of 2^4?

We know that $2^4 = 16$, so the unit digit is 6, however, if the question asks—what is the unit digit of 2^{17}?, then it would be a time-consuming exercise to calculate the value of 2^{17}.

Let us see the power cycle of '2'. It is $2, 4, 8, 16, 32, 64, 128, 256, 512, 1024, 2048, \ldots$ You may observe that the unit digit is the same for every 5th indexed number in the series. For example, the unit digit is '2' for 1st, 5th, 9th, 13th numbers in the series; while the unit digit is '8' for 3rd, 7th, 11th numbers in the series. So, for Base, '2', the unit digit repeats after every 4th cycle, so the power cycle of base '2' is '4'.

Table showing the power cycles of first 9 positive integers:

Base	Series	Digits of cycle	Cycle	Unit digit
0	0,0,0,0,...	0	1	0 for any exponent
1	1,1,1,1,...	1	1	1 for any exponent
2	2,4,8,16,32,64,128,256,512,...2,4,8 ,6	4	repeats after every 4th number
3	3,9,27,81,243,729,...	3,9,7,1	4	repeats after every 4th number
4	4,16,64,216....	4,6	2	repeats after every 2nd number
5	5,25,125,525,...	5	1	5 for any exponent
6	6,36,216,1264,...	6	6	6 for any exponent
7	7,49,343,2401,16807,...	7,9,3,1	4	repeats after every 4th number
8	8,64,512,4096,32768,...	8,4,2,6	4	repeats after every 4th number
9	9,81,729,...	9,1	4	repeats after every 4th number

Summary:

(1) The unit digits for the bases 0, 1, 5, & 6 are the bases itself.

(2) The unit digits for the bases 2, 3, 7, & 8 follow the cycle of '4'.

(3) The unit digits for the bases 4, & 9 follow the cycle of '2'.

Deduction of unit digit:

Example: What is the unit digit of 7^{34}?

Step1: Identify the base, its power cycle, and the exponent.
=> We know that the power cycle of the base, 7, is 4 (7,9,3,1), and the exponent is 34.

Step2: Divide the exponent by the power cycle, and get the remainder.
=> The remainder of 34/4 is 2.

Step3: Identify the digit of the power cycle corresponding to the remainder.
=> We know that the remainder is 2, and the power cycle of 7 is (7,9,3,1), hence the 2nd digit of the power cycle would be the unit digit of 7^{34}, which is 9: (7,**9**,3,1).

What if the questions had been: What is the unit digit of 7^{36}?

Again, we know that the power cycle of the base, 7, is 4 (7,9,3,1), and the exponent is 36 and dividing 36 by 4 gives a remainder "0". If the remainder is "0", we must take the last number in the power cycles which is "1". So the unit digit of 7^{36} is 1.

Example: What is the unit digit of $7^2.9^3.3^2$?

Step1: Deduce the unit digit of each number with exponent
=> The unit digit of 7^2 is "9"; similarly, the unit digit of 9^3 is "9"; similarly, the unit digit of 3^2 is "9".

Step2: Multiply all the unit digits deduced
=> The unit digit of $7^2.9^3.3^2$ => 9.9.9 = 9^3 is "9".

3.2.2 Roots and Surds

Root is a familiar word; you have heard this before—square root, and cube root etc..

Square root:

It is opposite of square. While square of a number means multiplying a number with itself to get a new number, "Square root" means to get a number such that multiplying it with itself would give the original number.

Example: Say a number is $x = 4$, then the 'square $= x^2 = 4^2 = 16$', and 'square root $= \sqrt[2]{x} = \sqrt[2]{4} = 2; 2 \times 2 = 4$'. Some consider that $\sqrt[2]{4} = 2$ or -2. However, it is not so. Its value is +2 only.

The confusion starts from here:

If $x^2 = 16$, what is x? While taking the square root of both the sides, we get $\sqrt[2]{x^2} = \sqrt[2]{16} => \pm x = 4 => x = \pm 4$!

Remember that **square** of a number is NOT always greater than its **square root.** If a number is $x = 4$, then the '$x^2 = 16$', and $\sqrt{x} = 2; 16 > 2$; however if a number is $x = 1/4$, then the '$x^2 = 1/16$', and '$\sqrt{x} = 1/2$'; $1/16 < 1/2$.

Square of a negative number is possible, but the **square root** is not possible, it would be an imaginary number. If a number is $x = -4$, then '$x^2 = 16$', and '$\sqrt{x} = \sqrt[2]{-2}$'; an imaginary number.

Cube root:

Like square root, which is opposite of square, cube root is opposite of cube. Cube of a number means multiplying a number with itself thrice to get a new number, "Cube root" means to get a number such that multiplying it with itself thrice would give the original number.

Example: Say a number is $x = 8$, then the 'cube $= x^3 = 8^3 = 512$', and 'cube root $= \sqrt[3]{x} = \sqrt[3]{8} = 2$'; $2 \times 2 \times 2 = 8$.

Like square, and its square root, **cube** of a number is NOT always greater than its **cube root.** If a number is $x = 8$, then the '$x^3 = 512$', and '$\sqrt[3]{x} = 2$'; $512 > 2$; however if a number is $x = 1/8$, then the '$x^3 = 1/512$', and '$\sqrt[3]{x} = 1/2$'; $1/512 > 1/2$.

Cube root gives unique value of x:

We have seen that if $x^2 = 4, => x = \pm 2.$; no unique value of x; it may be either 2 or -2. However if $x^3 = 8, => x = 2$; a unique value of x; because if $x = -2, x^3 = -8$. So cube root gives the unique value. This concept is widely tested in the Data Sufficiency questions.

n^{th} root:

Like square root, and cube root, n^{th} root means multiplying a number with itself n times to get the original number. Say a number is x, then its nth root would be $\sqrt[n]{x}$.

Example: Say a number is $x = 32$, $\sqrt[5]{32} = 2$; $2 \times 2 \times 2 \times 2 \times 2 = 32$.

3.2.2.1 Surds

If the root of a number renders an irrational number, its exponent is called **Surd**.

The square root of 2, $\sqrt[2]{2} = 1.414$; an irrational number, hence a surd.

You must know few values: $\boldsymbol{\sqrt{2} = 1.414}$, $\boldsymbol{\sqrt{3} = 1.732}$, $\boldsymbol{\sqrt{5} = 2.236}$.

3.2.2.2 Rationalization of surds

Keeping a surd in the denominator is not a standard way of writing a number or expression in mathematics. Surds should be placed in the numerator. If a number is $\frac{3}{\sqrt{2}}$, we can get rid of $\sqrt{2}$ placed in the denominator by multiplying and dividing the fraction by $\sqrt{2}$.

$$\Rightarrow \frac{3}{\sqrt{2}} = \frac{3}{\sqrt{2}} \times \left(\frac{\sqrt{2}}{\sqrt{2}}\right) = \frac{3\sqrt{2}}{(\sqrt{2})^2} = \frac{3\sqrt{2}}{2}.$$

Example 1: Rationalize $\dfrac{\sqrt{2}+1}{\sqrt{2}-1}$.

We cannot multiply the numerator and the denominator by $(\sqrt{2}-1)$ to remove the surd in the denominator; the denominator will result into $(\sqrt{2}-1)^2 = (\sqrt{2})^2 - 2.\sqrt{2}.1 + 1^2 = 2 - 2\sqrt{2} + 1 = 3 - 2\sqrt{2}$; again we would have a surd.

The optimum approach to do this is to make use of the formula $(a-b)(a+b) = a^2 - b^2$. Assume $a = \sqrt{2}$, and $b = 1$. By multiplying $\dfrac{\sqrt{2}+1}{\sqrt{2}+1}$ to the number, we will have a pair of $(\sqrt{2}-1)(\sqrt{2}+1)$ in the denominator, which will give $[(\sqrt{2})^2 - 1^2] = 2 - 1 = 1$; thus the surd is removed.

The term $(\sqrt{2}+1)$ is called the conjugate of $(\sqrt{2}-1)$.

$$\Rightarrow \frac{\sqrt{2}+1}{\sqrt{2}-1} \times \left(\frac{\sqrt{2}+1}{\sqrt{2}+1}\right) = \frac{(\sqrt{2}+1)^2}{(\sqrt{2})^2 - 1^2} = \frac{(\sqrt{2}+1)^2}{1} = (\sqrt{2}+1)^2.$$

Example 2: Rationalize $\dfrac{\sqrt{x}-\sqrt{y}}{\sqrt{x}+\sqrt{y}}$.

$$\Rightarrow \frac{\sqrt{x}-\sqrt{y}}{\sqrt{x}+\sqrt{y}} \times \left(\frac{\sqrt{x}-\sqrt{y}}{\sqrt{x}-\sqrt{y}}\right) = \frac{(\sqrt{x}-\sqrt{y})^2}{(\sqrt{x})^2+(\sqrt{y})^2} = \frac{(\sqrt{x}-\sqrt{y})^2}{x-y}; (\sqrt{x}-\sqrt{y}) \text{ is the conju-}$$

gate of $(\sqrt{x}+\sqrt{y})$.

Key: If the expression in the denominator has '+' sign, then multiply and divide the number with its conjugate, i.e. an expression with '−' sign and vice-versa. $(x-y)$ and $(x+y)$ are conjugates of each other.

3.3   Multiplication and Division of decimals with 10^x

We are often faced with multiplications such as 20.0987×10^3 or $\dfrac{5482.75}{10^{-4}}$. Follow the following approach to do such operations in less time.

Scenario 1:

If the exponent of base 10 is a positive integer.

Step 1: Move the decimal to its right number of times the exponent value

Step 2: If number of digits to the right of the decimal is less than the value of the exponent, add requisite number of '0s' after the last digit of the number

Example 1: 20.0987×10^3

The value of the exponent is 3. By moving the decimal to the right 3 times in the number 20.0987, we will get the number 20098.7.

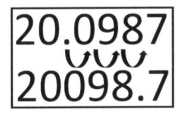

Scenario 2:

If the exponent of base 10 is a negative integer.

Step 1: Move decimal to its left number of times the exponent value

Step 2: If number of digits to the left of the decimal is less than the value of the exponent, add requisite number of '0s' before the first digit of the number

Example 2: 20.0987×10^{-3}

The value of the exponent is –3. By moving decimal to the left 3 times in the number 20.0987, we will get number the 0.0200987.

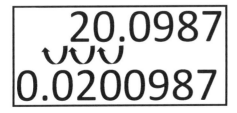

Example 3: $20.0987 \div 10^{-3}$?

First, convert division into multiplication. So, $20.0987 \div 10^{-3} = \frac{20.0987}{10^{-3}} = 20.0987 \times 10^3$. Now the question fits into scenario 1. Here, the value of the exponent is 3. By moving decimal to the right 3 times in the number 20.0987, we will get the number 20098.7.

In a nut shell, following numbers are equal; $20.0987 \times 10^3 = 2.00987 \times 10^4 = 0.200987 \times 10^5 = 200.987 \times 10^2 = 20098.7 = 200987 \times 10^{-1}$. Similarly, $\frac{20.0987}{100} = \frac{200.987}{1000} = \frac{2009.87}{10^4}$.

Example 4: $3,000,000 \times 0.0003$?

To transform the second number, 0.0003, equals to '3 times the exponent of 10', it needs an exponent of '4' to the base 10 or the multiplication of 10,000; we can borrow four '0s' from the first number, 3,000,000, so $3,000,000 \times 0.0003$ becomes 300.0000×3 equalling 900.

$$\boxed{3000000 \times 0.0003}$$

Example 5: $\dfrac{1.96[10^3(6.03 - 3 \times 10^{-2})]}{(1.4)^2} = ?$

$$\Rightarrow \frac{1.96[10^3(6.03 - 3 \times 10^{-2})]}{(1.4)^2} = \frac{\cancel{1.96}[10^3(6.03 - 3 \div 100)]}{\cancel{1.96}} = 10^3(6.03 - 3 \div 100)$$

$$\Rightarrow 10^3(6.03 - 0.03) = 1000 \times 6 = \mathbf{6000}.$$

3.4   Common Binomial expressions

(1) $a(b + c) = ab + ac$

=> $150 \times 51 = 150(50 + 1) = 150 \times 50 + 150 \times 1 = 7500 + 150 = 7650$

=> $38 \times 19 = 38(20 - 1) = 38 \times 20 - 38 \times 1 = 760 - 38 = 722$

(2) $(a + b)^2 = a^2 + 2ab + b^2$

=> $102^2 = (100 + 2)^2 = 100^2 + 2.100.2 + 2^2 = 10000 + 400 + 4 = 10404$

(3) $(a - b)^2 = a^2 - 2ab + b^2$

=> $98^2 = (100 - 2)^2 = 100^2 - 2.100.2 + 2^2 = 10000 - 400 + 4 = 9604$

(4) $(a^2 - b^2) = (a + b)(a - b)$

=> $98^2 - 2^2 = (98 + 2)(98 - 2) = 100 \times 96 = 9600$

(5) $(a + b + c)^2 = a^2 + b^2 + c^2 + 2(ab + bc + ca)$

(6) $(a + b)^3 = a^3 + 3a^2b + 3ab^2 + b^3$

=> $102^3 = (100 + 2)^3 = 100^3 + 3.100^2.2 + 3.100.2^2 + 2^3 = 1000000 + 60000 + 1200 + 8 = 1061208$

or $(a + b)^3 = a^3 + 3ab(a + b) + b^3$

=> $51^3 = (50 + 1)^3 = 50^3 + 3.50.1.(50 + 1) + 1^3 = 125000 + 150.51 + 1 = 132651$

(7) $(a - b)^3 = a^3 - 3a^2b + 3ab^2 - b^3$

=> $98^3 = (100 - 2)^3 = 100^3 - 3.100^2.2 + 3.100.2^2 - 2^3 = 1000000 - 60000 + 1200 - 8 = 941192$

or $(a - b)^3 = a^3 - 3ab(a - b) - b^3$

=> $49^3 = (50 - 1)^3 = 50^3 - 3.50.1.(50 - 1) - 1^3 = 125000 - 150.49 - 1 = 117649$

(8) $(a^3 + b^3) = (a + b)(a^2 - ab + b^2)$

=> $11^3 + 9^3 = (11 + 9)(11^2 - 11.9 + 9^2) = 20.(121 - 99 + 81) = 20.103 = 2060$

(9) $(a^3 - b^3) = (a - b)(a^2 + ab + b^2)$

=> $11^3 - 9^3 = (11 - 9)(11^2 + 11.9 + 9^2) = 2.(121 + 99 + 81) = 2.301 = 602$

3.5 Some important summation of series

(1) Sum of first positive integers $= 1 + 2 + 3 + 4 + 5 + \ldots\ldots\ldots n = \dfrac{n(n+1)}{2}$

Example: $12 + 13 + 14 + 15 + 16 + 17 + 18 =?$

$=> 12 + 13 + 14 + 15 + 16 + 17 + 18 = (1 + 2 + 3 + 4 + \ldots\ldots 18) - (1 + 2 + 3 + 4 + \ldots\ldots 11)$

$=> \dfrac{18(18+1)}{2} - \dfrac{11(12+1)}{2} = \dfrac{18.19}{2} - \dfrac{11.12}{2} = 171 - 66 = 105$

Alternate Approach:

$=> 12 + 13 + 14 + 15 + 16 + 17 + 18 = (11 + 1) + (11 + 2) + (11 + 3) + (11 + 4) + (11 + 5) + (11 + 6) + (11 + 7)$

$=> (11 + 11 + 11 + 11 + 11 + 11 + 11) + (1 + 2 + 3 + 4 + 5 + 6 + 7) = 77 + \left[\dfrac{7.8}{2}\right] = 77 + 28 = 105$

(2) Sum of squares of first positive integers $= 1^2 + 2^2 + 3^2 + 4^2 + 5^2 + \ldots\ldots\ldots n^2 = \dfrac{n(n+1)(2n+1)}{6}$

(3) Sum of cubes of first positive integers $= 1^3 + 2^3 + 3^3 + 4^3 + 5^3 + \ldots\ldots\ldots n^3 = \left[\dfrac{n(n+1)}{2}\right]^2$

(4) Sum of odd integers $= 1 + 3 + 5 + \ldots\ldots\ldots(2n-1) = n^2$

(5) Sum of even integers $= 2 + 4 + 6 + \ldots\ldots\ldots 2n = n(n+1)$

3.6 Fractions

Fraction is a number which is formed out of numerator and denominator. It is represented as $\dfrac{\text{Numerator}}{\text{Denominator}}$. Both numerator and denominator are integers, but none is equal to 0.

Example: $\dfrac{3}{4}, \dfrac{7}{8}, -\dfrac{9}{5}$ etc.

Proper fraction: For a fraction, if the absolute value of the numerator is less than the absolute value of the denominator, it is called a proper fraction. **Example:** $\frac{3}{4}, \frac{7}{8}, -\frac{9}{10}$ etc.

Improper fraction: If the absolute value of the numerator of a fraction is more than the absolute value of the denominator, it is called improper fraction. **Example:** $\frac{4}{3}, \frac{11}{8}, -\frac{9}{5}$ etc..

Mixed fraction: If the fraction is a mix of both an integer and proper fraction, it is called mixed fraction. **Example:** $2\frac{4}{3}, -5\frac{2}{3}$ etc.

Converting mixed fraction to improper fraction: Say, a mixed fraction is $5\frac{2}{3}$.

Step 1: Multiply the integer part with the denominator. $5 * 3 = 15$.
Step 2: Add the numerator to the number attained in step 1. So, $15 + 2 = 17$. It is the numerator of improper fraction.
Step 3: The equivalent improper fraction is $\frac{\text{new numerator}}{\text{denominator}} = \frac{5 \times 3 + 2}{3} = \frac{17}{3}$

Equivalent Fraction: Fractions that are equal in values are called equivalent fractions, although the numerator and denominator of the equivalent fractions may not be the same.

Example: $1/2 = 2/4 = 3/6 = 4/8 = 5/10$.

3.6.1 Concept of fraction

Let us understand the concept of fraction through graphical representation. Fraction is a part of a whole. For example, the fraction 3/8 means that out of 8 parts, only 3 parts are taken; it can also be thought of as eating 3 slices of pizza of an 8-slice pizza.

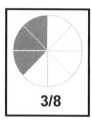

3/8

Reciprocal of fraction: You get reciprocal of a fraction when you interchange numerator and denominator. **Example:** Reciprocal of $\frac{3}{8}$ is $\frac{8}{3}$.

What is the significance of $\dfrac{8}{3}$?

To understand this, first convert $\frac{8}{3}$ into mixed fraction, which is $2\frac{2}{3}$. It means eating 2 full pizzas and 2 slices of pizza of a 3-slice pizza.

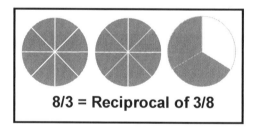

8/3 = Reciprocal of 3/8

Decimal Representation:

A fraction can be represented as a decimal number by dividing the numerator by the denominator. For example, the fraction 3/8 represents the numerical value 0.375; it is a decimal number.

Percent Representation:

A fraction can be represented as a percent by dividing the numerator by the denominator and then multiplying it by 100. For example, $3/4 = 0.75 => 0.75 \times 100\% = 75\%$ and similarly, $1/2 = 50\%$.

3.6.2 Mathematical operations on fractions

Mathematical operation	Example
Addition/ Subtraction	$\frac{1}{2} + \frac{1}{2} = 1$; two halves makes 1; $\frac{1}{2} - \frac{1}{4} =?$ => $\frac{1 \times 2}{2 \times 2} - \frac{1}{4} = \frac{2}{4} - \frac{1}{4} = \frac{2-1}{4} = \frac{1}{4}$; make denominators equal
Multiplication	$\frac{1}{2} \times \frac{1}{2} = \frac{1}{4}$; half of a half makes it $\frac{1}{4}$; $\frac{3}{5} \times \frac{15}{6} = \frac{3}{2}$; any numerator can cancel any denominator; two numerators will be multiplied, and similar, two denominators will be multiplied
Division	$\frac{1}{2} \div \frac{1}{2} = \frac{1}{2} \times \frac{2}{1} = 1$; '÷' will change to '×' and the fraction to the right will turn reciprocal; $\frac{3}{5} \div \frac{3}{5} = \frac{3}{5} \times \frac{5}{3} = 1$; a fraction divided by itself is always '1'; product of a fraction with its reciprocal is always 1.

Some confusing divisions:

- $\dfrac{2/3}{3/2} = \frac{2}{3} \div \frac{3}{2} = \frac{2}{3} \times \frac{2}{3} = \frac{4}{9}$;

- $\dfrac{2}{3/2} = 2 \div \frac{3}{2} = 2 \times \frac{2}{3} = \frac{4}{3}$;

- whereas $\dfrac{2/3}{3} = \frac{2}{3} \div 3 = \frac{2}{3} \times \frac{1}{3} = \frac{2}{9}$

Example: $\dfrac{2}{2 - \dfrac{2}{1 - \dfrac{4}{2 - \dfrac{5}{2 + \dfrac{6}{7}}}}} = ?$

=> Start solving from the lowermost fraction

$$\Rightarrow \cfrac{2}{2 - \cfrac{2}{1 - \cfrac{4}{2 - \cfrac{5}{2 + \cfrac{6}{7}}}}} = \cfrac{2}{2 - \cfrac{2}{1 - \cfrac{4}{2 - \cfrac{5}{\mathbf{\cfrac{2 \times 7 + 6}{7}}}}}} = \cfrac{2}{2 - \cfrac{2}{1 - \cfrac{4}{2 - \cfrac{5}{\mathbf{\cfrac{20}{7}}}}}};$$

Remember that the primary division operator is between "5" and "20". So $\cfrac{5}{\frac{20}{7}} = 5 \div \cfrac{20}{7} =$

$5 \times \cfrac{2}{3} = \cfrac{7}{20} = \cfrac{7}{4}$; Do not get it confused with $\cfrac{\frac{5}{20}}{7} \neq \cfrac{5}{\frac{20}{7}}$.

=> Coming back to the question:

$$\Rightarrow \cfrac{2}{2 - \cfrac{2}{1 - \cfrac{4}{2 - \cfrac{5}{\mathbf{\cfrac{20}{7}}}}}} = \cfrac{2}{2 - \cfrac{2}{1 - \cfrac{4}{2 - \cfrac{7 \times 5}{20}}}} = \cfrac{2}{2 - \cfrac{2}{1 - \cfrac{4}{\frac{7}{4}}}} = \cfrac{2}{2 - \cfrac{2}{1 - 4 \times 4}} = \cfrac{2}{2 - \cfrac{2}{1 - 16}} =$$

$$\cfrac{2}{2 - \cfrac{2}{-15}}$$

$$\Rightarrow \cfrac{2}{2 + \cfrac{2}{15}} = \cfrac{2}{\frac{32}{15}} = \cfrac{2 \times 15}{30} = \cfrac{15}{16}$$

3.6.3 Comparing fractions

You may come across situation where you have to compare the two fractions—which fraction is greater or smaller?

A general rule: For positive factions, larger the numerator, greater is the fraction (with the same denominator), and smaller the denominator, greater is the fraction (with the same numerator) and vice-versa; opposite is true for negative fractions.

Example 1: Which is greater $\frac{1}{2}$ or $\frac{1}{3}$? Well, this is a simple one as the numerators of the fractions are equal. For positive factions, if the numerators of the fractions are equal, the fraction with smaller denominator is greater, so $\frac{1}{2} > \frac{1}{3}$; however $-\frac{1}{2} < \frac{1}{3}$; $-\frac{1}{2} < -\frac{1}{3}$; $\frac{1}{2} > -\frac{1}{3}$.

Example 2: Which is greater $\frac{2}{5}$ or $\frac{3}{5}$? Again, this is a simple one as the denominator of the fractions are equal. For positive factions, if the denominators of the fractions are equal, the fraction with the larger numerator is greater, $\frac{2}{5} < \frac{3}{5}$; however $\frac{2}{5} > -\frac{3}{5}$; $-\frac{2}{5} > -\frac{3}{5}$; $\frac{2}{5} > -\frac{3}{5}$.

Example 3: Which is greater $\frac{11}{15}$ or $\frac{9}{16}$? This is the easiest of all to deduce. As the numerator of the first fraction is greater than that of the other and its denominator is smaller than that of the other, so on both the counts, the first fraction scores over the other, hence it is greater than the second fraction, so $\frac{11}{15} > \frac{9}{16}$; however $-\frac{11}{15} < -\frac{9}{16}$.

Example 4: Which is greater $\frac{5}{7}$ or $\frac{7}{9}$? This is not an easier one to deduce. The numerator of the first fraction is greater than that of the other but its denominator is also larger than that of the other, so on one count, the first fraction scores over the second and on the other count, the second one scores over the first. So how to deduce which fraction is greater? There are three approaches to deduce this.

Approach 1:

Convert fractions to Decimals

Each fraction can be converted into a decimal by dividing the numerator by the denominator. In decimal format, the value of each fraction can be compared.

$$=> \frac{5}{7} = 0.714; \quad \frac{7}{9} = 0.777, \text{ so } 0.777 > 0.714.$$

Since the decimal equivalent of 7/9 is larger than that of 5/7, so 7/9 > 5/7.

Approach 2:

Take 50%

The approach is to take 50% of the denominator and deduct it from the numerator, and then compare the remaining fractions.

Which is greater $\frac{5}{7}$ or $\frac{4}{5}$?

=> 50% of 7 (denominator of the first fraction) is 3.5, and 50% of 5 (denominator of the second fraction) is 2.5, so we can write $\left[\frac{5}{7} = \frac{3.5}{7} + \frac{1.5}{7} \right] <> \left[\frac{4}{5} = \frac{2.5}{5} + \frac{1.5}{5} \right]$

=> $(50\% + \frac{1.5}{7}) <> (50\% + \frac{1.5}{5})$ => It is obvious that $\frac{1.5}{7} < \frac{1.5}{5}$, so, $\frac{5}{7} < \frac{4}{5}$.

This approach may not be applicable in each case; after seeing all the approaches, you should decide which approach works best for a specific scenario.

Approach 3:

Cross Multiplication

Another approach to compare fractions is: Cross Multiplication. Numerator of the first fraction is multiplied to the denominator of the second fraction, and numerator of the second fraction is multiplied to the denominator of the first fraction. Now compare the results, and identify the greater of the two products; the fraction which has its numerator in the greater of the two products is a greater fraction than the other fraction.

=> Which is greater $\dfrac{5}{7}$ or $\dfrac{7}{9}$?

=> (Numerator of I * Denominator of II) = 5 * 9 = 45; (Numerator of II * Denominator of I) = 7 * 7 = 49, since 49 > 45 and "49" includes the numerator of the second fraction, hence the second fraction is greater than the first fraction.

3.6.4 More on fractions

(1) If $\dfrac{a}{b} > 1$, then $\dfrac{a+c}{b+c} < \dfrac{a}{b}$; where $a, b, \& c$ are positive numbers

=> Say $\dfrac{a}{b} = \dfrac{3}{2}$, and $c = 1$, then $\dfrac{a+c}{b+c} = \dfrac{3+1}{2+1} = \dfrac{4}{3} = 1.33 < \left[\dfrac{a}{b} = \dfrac{3}{2} = 1.5\right]$

We can understand it this way: Since the fraction a/b > 1, it means that a > b. When we add 'c' to each 'a' and 'b', larger proportion of 'c' is added to 'b' i.e. denominator and relatively a smaller proportion of 'c' is added to 'a' i.e. the numerator. Let us see how.

$$\dfrac{a+c}{b+c} = \dfrac{a\left(1+\dfrac{c}{a}\right)}{b\left(1+\dfrac{c}{b}\right)} = \dfrac{a}{b} \times \dfrac{\left(1+\text{smaller fraction compared to }\dfrac{c}{b}\right)}{\left(1+\text{larger fraction compared to }\dfrac{c}{a}\right)} = \left[\dfrac{a}{b} \times \dfrac{\text{smaller number}}{\text{larger number}}\right] < \dfrac{a}{b}$$

(2) If $\dfrac{a}{b} < 1$, then $\dfrac{a+c}{b+c} > \dfrac{a}{b}$; where $a, b, \& c$ are positive numbers

=> Say $\dfrac{a}{b} = \dfrac{2}{3}$, and $c = 1$, then $\dfrac{a+c}{b+c} = \dfrac{2+1}{3+1} = \dfrac{3}{4} = 0.75 > \left[\dfrac{a}{b} = \dfrac{2}{3} = 0.667\right]$

(3) If $\dfrac{a}{b} > 1$, then $\dfrac{a-c}{b-c} > \dfrac{a}{b}$; where $a, b, \& c$ are positive numbers

=> Say $\dfrac{a}{b} = \dfrac{3}{2}$, and $c = 1$, then $\dfrac{a-c}{b-c} = \dfrac{3-1}{2-1} = \dfrac{2}{1} = 2 > \left[\dfrac{a}{b} = \dfrac{3}{2} = 1.50\right]$

(4) If $\dfrac{a}{b} < 1$, then $\dfrac{a-c}{b-c} < \dfrac{a}{b}$; where $a, b, \& c$ are positive numbers

=> Say $\dfrac{a}{b} = \dfrac{2}{3}$, and $c = 1$, then $\dfrac{a-c}{b-c} = \dfrac{2-1}{3-1} = \dfrac{1}{2} = 0.50 < \left[\dfrac{a}{b} = \dfrac{2}{3} = 0.667\right]$

3.6.5 Fractions and their percent equivalents

Fraction	Percent	Fraction	Percent
$\dfrac{1}{1}$	100%	$\dfrac{1}{9}$	11.11%
$\dfrac{1}{2}$	50%	$\dfrac{1}{10}$	110%
$\dfrac{1}{3}$	33.33%	$\dfrac{1}{11}$	9.09%
$\dfrac{1}{4}$	25%	$\dfrac{1}{12}$	8.33%
$\dfrac{1}{5}$	20%	$\dfrac{1}{25}$	4%
$\dfrac{1}{6}$	16.67%	$\dfrac{1}{50}$	2%
$\dfrac{1}{7}$	14.28%	$\dfrac{1}{100}$	1%
$\dfrac{1}{8}$	12.50%	$\dfrac{1}{200}$	0.50%

Application:

How do you solve a question which asks *"If gasoline price increased by 10%, by what percent should one reduce its consumption so that the expense on gasoline remains the same?"*

Traditional Approach:

Say, before the increase, the price of gasoline was $100/gallon, and the consumption was 100 gallons. So, the expense = 100*100=$10000.

Now, after the increase, the price of gasoline is \$110/gallon (10% up), and say the consumption is reduced to x gallons. So, the expense=$110 \times x = \$110x$.

Since the expense needs to be the same as before, hence $10000 = 110x \Rightarrow x = 90.90$ gallons

$\Rightarrow$ Percent reduction in consumption $= \dfrac{100 - 90.90}{100} \times 100\% = 9.09\%$.

See-Saw Approach:

Scenario 1: When $x \times y = C$; where x is one element, y is second element, and C is a constant.

If x goes up by certain percent and y must go down with some percent such that after the change $x \times y = x' \times y' = C$, follow the following short-cut steps to get the answer. Where after the change, x becomes x', and y becomes y'.

Step 1: Covert the given percent figure into fraction, say it is $\frac{1}{a}$; you should take the help of the conversion table.
Step 2: Add "1" to the denominator of the fraction attained; it would be $\frac{1}{a+1}$.
Step 3: Convert $\frac{1}{a+1}$ fraction into percent; it is the requisite answer; you should take the help of the table.

Let us get the answer to the above question with the See-Saw approach.

Step 1: Price goes up by 10%; equivalent fraction of 10% is $\frac{1}{10}$, so $\frac{1}{a} = \frac{1}{10}$.
Step 2: By adding "1" to the denominator of the fraction $\frac{1}{a}$, we get $\frac{1}{a+1} = \frac{1}{11}$.
Step 3: With the help of the table, we get $\frac{1}{11} = 9.09\%$; it is the requisite answer. The consumption must go down by 9.09%.

Pl. see the pictorial representation of the See-Saw approach.

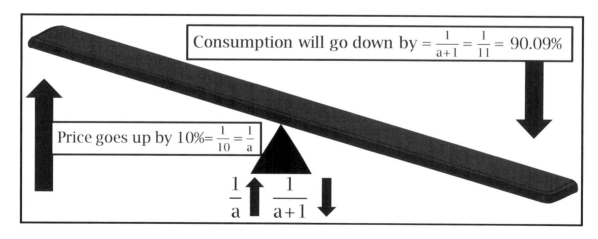

Scenario 2: When $x \times y = C$; where x is one element, y is second element, and C is constant.

If x goes down by certain percent and y must go up with some percent such that after the change $x \times y = x' \times y' = C$, follow the following short-cut steps to get the answer.

Step 1: Covert the given percent figure into fraction, say it is $\frac{1}{a}$; take the help of the table.
Step 2: Subtract "1" from the denominator of the fraction attained; it would be $\frac{1}{a-1}$
Step 3: Convert $\frac{1}{a-1}$ fraction into percent; it is the requisite answer; you should take the help of the table.

Let us apply the See-Saw approach in another question: *"If milk price decreased by 10%, by what percent should one increase its consumption so that the expense on milk remains the same?"*

Step 1: Price goes down by 10%; equivalent fraction of 10% is $\frac{1}{10}$, $\frac{1}{10}$, so $\frac{1}{a} = \frac{1}{10}$;
Step 2: By subtracting "1" from the denominator of the fraction $\frac{1}{a}$, we get $\frac{1}{a-1} = \frac{1}{9}$.
Step 3: With the help of the table, we get $\frac{1}{9} = 11.11\%$; it is the requisite answer. The consumption must go up by 11.11%.

Pl. see the pictorial representation of the same.

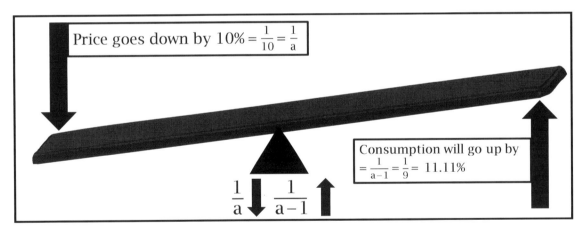

Example 1: If the sale of a brand is reduced by 17%, by what percent should the company increase its sales price such that the revenue earned remains the same as before?

    A. 14.28%

    B. 14.53%

    C. 20%

    D. 20.48%

First, identify whether the question fits into the category discussed above. Since "Quantity * Price = Revenue", and the condition is that the revenue must remain constant, hence the question fits into the See-Saw approach model. Out of the two scenarios, the second scenario fits as an element goes down and the complementary element must go up.

When we look at the table, we do not find 17%, however we can safely assume that it is closer to 16.67%; so the equivalent of 17% $=\approx$ 16.67% $=\approx \frac{1}{6} = \frac{1}{a} => \frac{1}{a-1} = \frac{1}{5} = 20\%$. The sales price must be increased by 20%. The correct answer would be a little more than 20% as we approximated 17% to 16.67%. So, the correct answer must be option D—the only greater option than 20%. The company should increase the sales price of the brand by 20.48%.

Example 2: If the price of milk increased by 11%, by what percent should its consumption be reduced such that the expenses on milk remains the same as before?

We identified that the question fits into the category discussed above, and it fits into the first scenario. Now, 11% $=\approx$ 11.11% $= \frac{1}{9} = \frac{1}{a} => \frac{1}{a+1} = \frac{1}{10} =\approx 10\%$.. The correct answer would be a little less than 10%.

3.7   Ratio & Proportion

Ratio is a relationship among two or more quantities; it is important that the units of the quantities considered are same.

We normally refer ratio in daily life. **Examples**: Ratio of number of boys to that of girls in a class is 2:3; Ratio of milk to water in a pot is 4:7, etc.

Ratio values are easier to refer and compare, but they are not absolute values. For the sake of comparison, instead of saying that region X has 100,000 cars and 50,000 two-wheelers; we can reduce both the numbers to relate them conveniently.

$$\frac{\text{\# of Cars}}{\text{\# of Two-wheelers}} = \frac{C}{T} = \frac{100,000}{50,000} = \frac{2}{1}$$

=> C : T = 2 : 1; It means that for every two-wheeler, there are two cars in the region X.

Terms used:

The first term, 2, of the ratio C : T = 2 : 1 is called **antecedent**, and the second term, 1, is called **consequent**.

Example 1: Two quantities are in the ratio of 5:7. If the first quantity is 155, find the second quantity.

Ratio values		Actual values		
Qty 1 :	Qty 2 ::	Qty 1 :	Qty 2	
5 :	7 ::	155 :	?(x)	

$$=> \frac{5}{7} = \frac{155}{x}$$

$$=> 5x = 7 \times 155 => x = \frac{7 \times 155}{5} = 217$$

Some rules:

(1) Multiplying the antecedent and the consequent of the ratio with the same number does not make it a different ratio; it will be called an equivalent ratio.

$$=> \frac{C}{T} = \frac{2}{1} = \frac{2 \times 10}{1 \times 10} = \frac{20}{10} = \frac{30}{15} = \frac{40}{20} = \frac{100,000}{50,000}$$

(2) We cannot get the actual values of the quantities compared from the ratio; we can only compare their relative values.

=> From the ratio C : T = 2 : 1, we cannot assume that the actual value of number of cars is 100,000 and that of two-wheelers is 50,000.

(3) Units of the quantities compared must be the same.

=> If the weights of three objects A, B and C are 1 ton, 500 kilograms, and 500 grams respectively, then what is the ratio of their weights?

First, convert each unit of measurement into single units of measurement convenient to you. It's better that we convert ton and gram into kilogram.

=> Weight of object A = 1 ton = 1000 kg.; Weight of object C = 500 grams = 1/2 kg.

So, the ratio of Wt. of A : Wt. of B : Wt. of C :: 1000 : 500: 1/2 => 2000 : 1000 : 1 (Multiplying by "2" throughout to get integer values.)

Example 2: A cask contains an 80 liter mixture of milk and water in the ratio of 69 : 31. By what percent of the mixture is milk more than water?

=> Given is, M : W :: 69 : 31; we want $\dfrac{\text{Milk} - \text{Water}}{\text{Mixture}(80)} \times 100\%$. It would be time-consuming to calculate the quantity of milk and water as the ratio values are in odd numbers. Let us apply the following approach.

=> **Ratio scale:**

M	:	W	:	Mixture (M + W)	:	(M − W)
69	:	31	:	(69+31)	:	(69 − 31)
				100	:	38

=> answer is $(38/100) \times 100\% = 38\%$.

3.7.1 Proportion

Proportion is the equality of two ratios. **Example:** 2 : 3 :: 4 : 6.

Types of proportions:

(A) **Direct proportion:** Two quantities are said to be in direct proportion if an increase in one quantity results in a proportional increase in the other quantity; and similarly, a decrease in one quantity results in a proportional decrease in the other quantity.

    Example: If the price of one phone is $300, the cost of two phones would be $600.

Phone1 : Phone2 :: Price1 : Price2

1   :   2   ::   300   :   ?(x)

$$=> \frac{1}{2} = \frac{300}{x} => x = 2 \times 300 = \$600.$$

(B) **Inverse proportion:** Two quantities are said to be in indirect or inverse proportion if an increase in one quantity results in a proportional decrease in the other quantity, and vice versa.

Example 3: If 3 men can complete a task in 2 days, in how many days will 6 men complete the task?

Men1 : Men2 :: Days2 : Days1

3   :   6   ::   ?(x) :   2

$$=> \frac{3}{6} = \frac{x}{2} => x = 1 \text{ day.}$$

(C) **Variation:** A quantity in ratio may increase or decrease w.r.t. power or exponent of other quantity.

Example 4: If the price of diamond varies with square of the size of the diamond, and the price of a diamond A is \$1000, then what is the price of the diamond B which is double the size of diamond A?

=> Price $\propto$ (Size)^2 => Price $= K.$(Size)^2; where K is a constant

So, we can write, PriceA $= K.$(SizeA)^2 & PriceB $= K.$(SizeB)^2

So, $\dfrac{\text{PriceA}}{\text{PriceB}} = \dfrac{K.(\text{SizeA})^2}{K.(\text{SizeB})^2}$

PriceA : PriceB :: (SizeA)^2 : (SizeB)^2

1000   :   ?(x) :: 1^2 : 2^2

1000   :   ?(x) ::   1   : 4

=> $x = 4 \times 1000 = \$4000/-$; Assume that the size of diamond A is 1 unit.

Diamond B will cost \$4000/-.

Example 5: If the efficiency of a machine varies inversely with the cube of length of time it worked, and its efficiency is 90% for 6 hours it worked, then what would be its efficiency if it worked for 10 hours?

$$\Rightarrow \text{Efficiency} \propto \frac{1}{(\text{time})^3} \Rightarrow \text{Eff.} = \frac{K}{(\text{time})^3}; \text{ where K is a constant}$$

So, we can write, $\text{Eff.}(90\%) = \dfrac{K}{(\text{time@}90\%)^3}$, and $\text{Eff.}(x\%) = \dfrac{K}{(\text{time@}x\%)^3}$

So, $\dfrac{\text{Eff.}(90\%)}{\text{Eff.}(x\%)} = \dfrac{(\text{time@}x\%)^3}{(\text{time@}90\%)^3}$

Eff.(90%)	:	Eff.(x%)	::	(time@x%)³	:	(time@90%)³
90%	:	?(x)	::	10^3	:	6^3

$$\Rightarrow x = \frac{90\%.6.6.6}{10.10.10} = 19.44\%$$

3.7.2 Role of common factor

Example 6: Two quantities are in the ratio of 5:7. If the first quantity is 155, find the second quantity.

Though we have dealt this question before, for the sake of understanding the role of common factor, we look at it again. Since the antecedent, 5, and the consequent, 7, show relative values, hence there must be a common factor between them; say it is x.

So, the actual values would be $5x$, and $7x$, hence we can deduce that $5x = 155 \Rightarrow x = 31$; so $7x = 7 \times 31 = 217$. The second quantity is 217.

Example 7: Two quantities are in the ratio of $2 : 7$. If each of them is increased by 14, then their ratio become $4 : 7$. Find the numbers.

Say the common factor is x, so the quantities are $2x$ and $7x$. After the increase, the quantities become $2x + 14$ and $7x + 14$. So we can write:

$$\Rightarrow \frac{2x + 14}{7x + 14} = \frac{4}{7} \Rightarrow 7(2x + 14) = 4(7x + 14) \Rightarrow x = 3.$$

So the quantities are $2x = 2.3 = 6$ and $7x = 7.3 = 21$.

3.8 Percents

Percent is the most used concept is Arithmetic. When we quote a relative figure, we mostly refer it w.r.t. 100.

Example: In a class, there are 20 boys and 30 girls. How many percent of boys are there in the class?

$$=> \% = \frac{\text{Value}}{\text{Total}} \times 100\% = \frac{\text{Number of boys}}{\text{Total number of students}} \times 100\% = \frac{20}{20 + 30} \times 100\% = 2050 \times 100\% = 40\%.$$

3.8.1 Smart calculation

Calculating the percent values may be time-consuming for some. Here are few smart techniques to make things easier. If you wish to calculate 10% of 5640, you may do it traditionally: 10% of 5640 $= \frac{10}{100} \times 5640 = 564$.

The table below shows how to calculate some common percent values with a smarter approach.

Calculating __ % of a number	Smarter approach
10% of a number	Move decimal one place from right to left. So, the 10% of 5640 would be 564.
5% of a number	Calculate 10% and then make it half. So, the 5% of 5640 would be (10% of 5640)/2 = 564/2 = 282.
1% of a number	Move decimal two places from right to left. So, the 1% of 5640 would be 56.40.
2% of a number	Calculate 1% and then double it. So, the 2% of 5640 would be 2*(1% of 5640) = 2*56.40 = 112.80.
0.5% of a number	Calculate 1% and divide it by 2. So, 0.5% of 5640 would be 56.40/2 = 28.20.

11% of a number	Calculate 10% and 1%, and then add them. So, the 11% of 5640 would be (10% of 5640 + 1% of 5640) = 564 + 56.40 = 620.40.
100% of a number	100% of the number is number itself. So, the 100% of 5640 would be 5640.
50% of a number	Calculate one-half of the number. So, the 50% of 5640 would be (1/2 of 5640) = 2820.
25% of a number	Calculate one-fourth of the number. So, the 25% of 5640 would be (1/4 of 5640) = 1410.
12.50% of a number	Calculate 25% and then make it half. So, the 12.5% of 5640 would be (25% of 5640)/2 = 1410/2 = 705. Alternatively, you can calculate one-eight of the number. So, the 12.5% of 5640 would be (1/8 of 5640) = 705.
33.33% of a number	Calculate one-third of the number. So, the 33.33% of 5640 would be (1/3 of 5640) = 1880.
75% of a number	Calculate three-fourth of the number. So, the 75% of 5640 would be (3/4 of 5640) = 3*1410 = 4230. Alternatively, you can calculate one-fourth of the number, and deduct it from the number. So, the 75% of 5640 would be (5640 – 1/4 of 5640) = 4230.
20% of a number	Calculate one-fifth of the number. So, the 20% of 5640 would be (1/5 of 5640) = 1128.
90% of a number	Calculate 10% of the number and deduct it from the number. So, the 90% of 5640 would be (5640 – 10% of 5640) = 5076.

3.8.2 Some applications

(A) Percentage increase or decrease

You may have to calculate the percent increase or decrease in value. Say, for example, if the population of a city rose from 45 million in the year 2011 to 50 million in the year 2012, then what is the percentage increase in the population of the city?

$$\Rightarrow \% \text{ increase} = \frac{\text{New value} - \text{Base value}}{\text{Base value}} \times 100\%$$

$$\Rightarrow \% \text{ increase in population} = \frac{\text{Population in yr. 2012} - \text{Population in yr. 2011}}{\text{Population in yr. 2011}} \times 100\%$$

$$\Rightarrow \% \text{ increase in population} = \frac{50-45}{45} \times 100\% = \frac{5}{45} \times 100\% = 11.11\%$$

(B) Beware of word *than*

If the question asks— *By what percent is the population in the year 2011 less than that in the year 2012?*

Will the answer be 11.11%?—No. It is not. In this question, the base of comparison is changed to the year 2012. Year 2012 will appear as base in the denominator.

$$\Rightarrow \% \text{ decrease in population} = \frac{\text{Population in yr. 2012} - \text{Population in yr. 2011}}{\text{Population in yr. 2012}} \times 100\%$$

$$\Rightarrow \% \text{ decrease in population} = \frac{50-45}{50} \times 100\% = \frac{5}{50} \times 100\% = 10\%$$

(C) Not always Percentage increase or decrease

(a) If the question asks — *What percent is the population in the year 2011 of the population in the year 2012?*

We need NOT calculate % increase or decrease here.

$$\Rightarrow \frac{\text{Population in yr. 2011}}{\text{Population in yr. 2012}} \times 100\% = \frac{45}{50} \times 100\% = 90\%$$

(b) Similarly, if the question asks — *What percent is the population in the year 2012 of the population in the year 2011?*

$$\Rightarrow \frac{\text{Population in yr. 2012}}{\text{Population in yr. 2011}} \times 100\% = \frac{50}{45} \times 100\% = 111.11\%$$

(D) Determine increased or decreased value

(a) If the question asks — *What would be the population in the year 2013, if the population grows at the same rate as during the period 2011–2012?*

We have already calculated % increase in the population equaling 11.11%. Applying traditional approach to solve this question is time-consuming. As per the traditional approach, we calculate the increase first, and then add the increase to the population in the year 2012 to get the population in the year 2013.

Following approach will save your precious time.

=> $\textbf{Population}|_{2013} = \textbf{Population}|_{2012} \times (1 + \% \textbf{ increase})$

=> $50 \times (1 + 11.11\%) = 50 \times (1 + 0.111) = 50 \times 1.11 = 55.55$ million

(b) Similarly, if the question is —*What would be company X's revenue for next year if it decreased by 23.87% from the current year revenue of $237.48 million?*

Following approach will save your precious time.

=> $\textbf{Revenue}|_{\text{nxt. Yr.}} = \textbf{Revenue}|_{\text{Current Yr.}} \times (1 - \% \textbf{ increase})$

=> $\text{Revenue}|_{\text{nxt. Yr.}} = 237.48 \times (1 - 0.2389) = 237.48 \times 0.7613$

Calculating 237.48*0.7613 without the help of calculator is frustrating. You can even save more time by truncating the decimals and approximating the number.

=> $\text{Revenue}|_{\text{nxt. Yr.}} = 237.48 \times (1- \approx 0.24) = 237.48 \times \approx 0.76 = 237.48 \times 0.75 = \approx 240 \times \frac{3}{4} = \approx 180$ million

(E) (Percent − Percent) ≠ Percent

If the question asks—*A shopkeeper used to charge 15% margin on its products. Due to competition, he revised the margin to 10%. By what percent did the shopkeeper decrease his margin?*

The answer is certainly not 5%.

Say, the sales is $100, then the margin charged earlier = 15% of 100 = $15, and the margin charged now = 10% of 100 = $10.

% decrease in margin = $\frac{15-10}{15} \times 100\% = 33.33\%$. So, the shopkeeper reduced its margin by 33.33%.

So, what does 15% – 10% represent?

In fact, **Percent – Percent = Percent Point**

Alternatively, we can also say that the shopkeeper reduced his margin by **5% points.**

(F) **Percent of what**

If the question asks — *If 80% of students play soccer and 25% of them joined a professional club, what percentage of of the total students in the school did not join the club?*

The answer is not 75% (100% – 25%). We must pay attention to the verbiage. It is not always that an entity is a percentage of total.

Here, the number of students joined club = 25% of 80% = $\frac{25}{100} \times 80\% = 20\%$. So, 20% joined the club, and 80% of students did not join the club.

(G) **Successive percent**

Calculating percents one after another is called successive percents. This concept is applied in case of calculating 'successive discounts' or 'successive profits' and also in cases when 'a quantity is expressed as a product of two other quantities'.

If the question asks—*A shopkeeper offers a discount of 20% on the MRP, and then further a discount of 10% on the invoice value. How much a customer will have to pay for a camera whose MRP is $200?*

Total discount offered by the shopkeeper is not 30% (20% + 10%). The reference values on which each discount was offered is different; while the first discount was offered on the MRP, the other one was offered on the invoice value.

Say the MRP is $100/-; so the invoice value after discount = MRP – Discount = 100–20 = $80, hence amount paid by the customer = Invoice value – II discount = 80 – 10% of 80 = 80 – 8 = 72%. So the customer paid 72% of $200 = $144 for the camera.

If there are $d_1, d_2, \& d_3$ % successive discounts, then the final price can be calculated in the following way.

=> **Price after discount = MRP** $\left(1 - \dfrac{\mathbf{d_1}}{\mathbf{100}}\right)\left(1 - \dfrac{\mathbf{d_2}}{\mathbf{100}}\right)\left(1 - \dfrac{\mathbf{d_3}}{\mathbf{100}}\right)$

Alternate approach:

If $x\%$ and $y\%$ are two successive percentage changes, the overall percentage change is given by:

$$\left(x + y + \frac{x \times y}{100}\right)\%;$$

where x and y are taken with their sign i.e. '+' for increase and '-' for decrease.

Applying this in the above question: Total discount $= -20 - 10 + \dfrac{-20 \times -10}{100} = -28\%$ discount. Thus, the customer pays $(100 - 28)\%$ of \$200 $= 72\%$ of \$200 $=$ \$144.

Another example:

Say, the length of a rectangle is increased by 10% and the breadth is decreased by 5%. What is the percentage change in the area of the rectangle?

We know that Area of Rectangle = Length * Breadth i.e. a quantity (Area) is expressed as a product of two quantities (Length and Breadth). Thus, we can use the concept of successive % change.

The overall percentage change in area $= +10 - 5 + \dfrac{10 \times -5}{100} = 5 - 0.5 = 4.5\%$ (Positive implies an increase in area).

(H) Number of times and percent

Few short cuts:

Question	Traditional approach	Smarter approach
If X is increased by 3 times, X now is what percent of the original value?	Say, X =100, then $X_{now} = 100 + 3 * 100 = 400$; $X_{now} = \frac{400}{100} \times 100\%$ of X = 400% of X	If X increased by n times, then $X_{now} = (1 + n) * 100\%$ of X; Or, X increased by $100n\%$. $X_{now} = (1 + 3) * 100\% X = 400\%$ of X
If X is increased by 300%, how many times is X now of the original value?	Say, X =100, then $X_{now} = 100 + 300\%$ of $100 = 400$; $X_{now} = \frac{400}{100} \times X = 4X$	If X increased by y %, then $X_{now} = (1 + \frac{y}{100}) * X$; Or, X increased by $\frac{y}{100}$ times. $X_{now} = (1 + 3) * X = 4X$
Price of a commodity costing $250 increased by 10%. What is the price after increase?	New Price = Old Price + Increase; $= 250 + \left(250 \times \frac{10}{100}\right) = \$275$	If the price is increased by y %, then New Price = Old Price*(1+y %) = 250*1.1 = $275; Or, X increased by y %. New Price = 110% of Old Price

(i) X is less than Y by 30% => It is same as saying X = 70% of Y => X = 0.7Y.

(ii) X is more than Y by 230% => It is better, you do as X = 330% of Y => X = 3.3Y.

(iii) X is less than Y by 60%, and Z is more than X by 50%.

=> It is better you do as X = 40% of Y => X = 0.4Y, and Z = 150% of X => Z = 1.5X => Z = 1.5*0.4Y = 0.6Y.

3.9 Translating words into math

Often times it is observed that once you get an algebraic equation in hand, it is easier to solve it and get the desired value(s) of variable(s). However, especially in arithmetic where you will find that the math is trapped in English language, and you have to extract math out of it. We bring you some examples to understand the math part in question narrations.

Example 1: What is 75% of 200?

The question wants us to find out the value of 75% of the number 200. Let us interpret each word in the question narration. "What = ?", "is = =", & "of = × (Multiplication)"

What	is	75 %	of	200	?
? Say x	=	75%	×	200	$x = 75\% \times 200$

Example 2: 150 is how much percent of 200?

150	is	how much %	of	200	?
150	=	Say $x\%$	×	200	$150 = x\% \times 200$

Example 3: Find a fraction that bears the same ratio to 1/27 that 3/7 does to 5/9.

Find a fraction that bears the same ratio	to	1/27	that	3/7	does to	5/9	.
Say x	:	1/27	=	3/7	:	5/9	$\dfrac{x}{\frac{1}{27}} = \dfrac{\frac{3}{7}}{\frac{5}{9}}$ $=> 27x = \dfrac{3 \times 9}{7 \times 5}$

Example 4: If A earns 30% more than B, by what percent is B's income less than that of A?

A	earns	30%	more than	B,	by what per-cent	is	B's in-come	less than that of A?
A	=	30%	+	B,	x	=	(B	$\dfrac{(A - B)}{A} \times 100\%$
A = 130				Say B = 100	$x = \left(\dfrac{A - B}{A}\right) \times 100\%$; Taking care of sign			

Example 5: Fee for an exhibition was $2. It was reduced by 25%, this resulted in an increase in sale by 20%. Find the percentage increase in the number of visitors.

Fee for an exhibition	was	$2.	It was reduced by 25%,	this resulted in increase in sales by 20%.	Find the percentage increase in the number of visitors.
x	=	$2	$y = x - 25\%$ of x $= 75\%$ of x $= 0.75x = 1.50$	Say sales (before) = $100; Sales (now) = $120	$\dfrac{\#\,(\text{now}) - \#\,(\text{before})}{\#(\text{before})} \times 100\%$ $\#(\text{before}) = \$100/2 = 50;$ $\#(\text{now}) = \$120/1.50 = 80$

3.10 Interest

We all know that borrowing money is not a free service. The money paid back to the lender over and above the borrowed sum is called **Interest**.

Key terms:

Principal or Sum borrowed: The money borrowed is called Principal or Sum. It is normally denoted by a symbol P.

Interest: The money paid back over and above the borrowed sum is called Interest. It is normally denoted by a symbol I.

Amount: The money paid back to the lender along with the interest is called Amount. Amount = Sum + Interest. It is normally denoted by a symbol A.

Rate of interest:

'100' is a base or reference value for calculating interest. So if the principal =100, and the interest = 10, then we can say that the rate of interest is 10%. It is normally denoted by a symbol r.

Period of borrowing:

The money borrowed is usually taken on loan for a certain period, say—a year, 6 months, 3 months, 1 month or even for a few days. So it is important to specify that for what period of time, the rate of interest is applicable. Saying 'r = 10%' is an incomplete information; one must say 'r=10% per annum' or some specific time period.

3.10.1 Simple Interest

Say a sum of $1000 is borrowed at a rate of 10% per annum for 2 years; the interest for the first year would be $\left[1000 \times \dfrac{10}{100} = \$100 \right]$. Similarly the interest for the second year would be another $100. So total interest for 2 years = $200. We can make a formula out of it.

$SI = \dfrac{P \times r \times t}{100}$ or $SI = \dfrac{Prn}{100}$; where SI is simple interest, P is sum borrowed, and t or n is time period.

Example 1: A man borrowed $16000 at a rate of $12\frac{1}{2}$% per annum for $6\frac{1}{2}$ years. How much amount shall he pay back to the lender?

$$\Rightarrow SI = \dfrac{P \times r \times t}{100} = \dfrac{16000 \times (25/2) \times (13/2)}{100} = \dfrac{16000 \times 25 \times 13}{100 \times 2 \times 2} = \$13000/\text{-}$$

=> Amount A = Principal + Interest = P + I = 16000 + 13000 = $29000/-.

The man will pay back $29000/- to the lender.

Example 2: If $450 amounts to $504 in 3 years, what will $615 amount to in $2\frac{1}{2}$ years?

=> Given that A = 504, and P = 450, so SI = A–P = 504 – 450 = 54.

$$\Rightarrow SI = \frac{P \times r \times t}{100} \Rightarrow 54 = \frac{450 \times r \times 3}{100} \Rightarrow r = \frac{54 \times 100}{450 \times 3} = 4\%$$

$$\Rightarrow \text{Again, SI for } \$615 = \frac{615 \times 4 \times (5/2)}{100} = \$61.50$$

=> Amount = A = P + I = 615 + 61.50 = $676.50.

$615 will amount to $676.50 in $2\frac{1}{2}$ years.

3.10.2 Compound Interest

In case of simple interest, the interest for the first period of time, the second period of time, the third period of time and onwards remain the same. However if the borrower and the lender agree on an agreement that the amount at the end of the first period of time will become the principal for the second period of time, and the amount at the end of the second period of time will become the principal for the third period of time onwards, then this arrangement is called **compounding.** It is called compounding because for every successive period of time, the principal is more than that of the previous period of time or in other words, the interest gets compounded.

Let's see an example if the conditions of lending are: (a) simple interest and (b) compound interest.

Example 3: A man borrowed $10000 at a rate of 10% per annum for 3 years. How much shall he pay back to the lender if the interest payable is: (a) simple interest and (b) compound interest?

Year	Simple interest	Compound interest
First	SI = 10000 × 10% = $1000	CI = 10000 × 10% = $1000; A = P + I = 10000 + 1000 = $11000; I = CI for the first period of time.
Second	SI = 10000 × 10% = $1000	CI = 11000 × 10% = $1100; Amount of the previous year = Principal of the current year; A = P + I = 11000 + 1100 = $12100; CI > SI for the second period of time.
Third	SI = 10000 × 10% = $1000	CI = 12100 × 10% = $1210; Amount of the previous year = Principal of the current year; A = P + I = 12100 + 1210 = $13310; CI for the third period of time > CI for the second period of time.
	Total SI = $3000	Total CI = 13310 – 10000 = $3310
	Amount = $13000	**Amount = $13310**

*If the question does not specify whether the interest is compound interest or simple interest, you should consider it as simple interest.

Formula:

$$A = P\left(1 + \frac{r}{100}\right)^n$$; where A = Amount, P = Principal, r = Rate of interest, and n = Period

The above question can be solved with the help of this formula.

$$A = P\left(1 + \frac{r}{100}\right)^n = 10000\left(1 + \frac{10}{100}\right)^3 = 10000\left(1 + \frac{1}{10}\right)^3 = 10000\left(\frac{11}{10}\right)^3 = \frac{10000 \times 11 \times 11 \times 1}{10 \times 10 \times 10}$$

$13310.

So, CI = A – P = 13310 – 10000 = $3310.

3.10.2.1 Half-Yearly and Quarterly compounding

We have been referring to time as a period. The time is not necessarily in years only. The compounding of interest can be half-yearly (6 months), quarterly (3 months), or even monthly.

Half-yearly compounding means the interest would be calculated two times in a year; similarly, quarterly compounding means the interest would be calculated four times in a year, and like-wise for monthly.

Example 4: A man borrowed $10000 at a rate of 10% per annum for 1 years. How much shall he pay back to the lender if the interest payable is calculated on (a) half-yearly compounding and (b) quarterly compounding basis?

(a) **Half-yearly compounding:**

=> P = 10000, r = 10% p.a., t = 1 years

Step 1: Covert rate of interest r = 10% p.a. into half yearly rate, so effective $r = 10\%/2 = 5\%$ per 6-months

Step 2: Covert time in years into periods; n = 1 years * 2 = 2 periods of 6-months

Step 3: Apply CI formula

$$A = P\left(1 + \frac{r}{100}\right)^n = 10000\left(1 + \frac{10/2}{100}\right)^{1\times2} = 10000\left(1 + \frac{1}{20}\right)^2 = 10000\left(\frac{21}{20}\right)^2 =$$
$11025.

(b) **Quarterly compounding:**

=> P = 10000, r = 10% p.a., t = 1 years

$$A = P\left(1 + \frac{r}{100}\right)^n = 10000\left(1 + \frac{10/4}{100}\right)^{1\times4} = 10000\left(1 + \frac{1}{40}\right)^4 = 10000\left(\frac{41}{40}\right)^4 =$$
$11038.

As you see that the amount after compounding the sum on quarterly basis ($11038) is more than that on half-yearly basis ($11025), we can conclude that as the period of compounding increases, the interest increases.

3.10.2.2 Calculating Rate of Interest and Time

Example 5: If a sum, compounding annually doubles itself in 4 years, what is the rate of interest?

A. 9.89%
B. 18.92%
C. 24.89%

Say P = 100, so A = 200, and n = 4 years.

$$=> 200 = 100\left(1 + \frac{r}{100}\right)^4 => 2 = \left(1 + \frac{r}{100}\right)^4;$$

$$=> 2^{1/4} = 1 + \frac{r}{100};$$

It is difficult to calculate r without scientific calculator as the normal calculator provided to you cannot calculate the 4th root. So, let us empty another approach to calculate $2^{1/4}$.

We can write $2^{1/4} = 1 + \frac{r}{100}$ as following.

$$=> (2^{1/2})^{1/2} = 1 + \frac{r}{100}$$

Now calculating $2^{1/2}$ is easy as the "Square-root" function is available on the GRE calculator.

$$=> (2^{1/2})^{1/2} = 1 + \frac{r}{100}$$

$$=> (1.414)^{1/2} = 1 + \frac{r}{100}; 2^{1/2} = 1.414$$

$$=> 1.189 = 1 + \frac{r}{100}$$

$$=> 0.189 = \frac{r}{100}$$

$$=> r = 18.9\%$$

Option B is the closest, so, option B is the correct answer.

Alternate Approach:

Remember that if a sum of money P becomes double at interest r and time n under compound interest, then an approximate result may be used: $r * n =\approx 72$ (provided r is small).

Here, $r * n =\approx 72$, where n = 4 (given). Thus, $r =\approx 72/4 =\approx 18\%$.

Example 6: If a sum compounding annually becomes 1.331 times of itself at a rate of 10%, what is the time period in years?

A. 2
B. 3
C. 4

Say P = 100, so A = 1.331 * 100 = 133.1, and r = 10%.

$\Rightarrow 133.1 = \left(1 + \dfrac{10}{100}\right)^n \Rightarrow 1.331 = (1.1)^n$; again by hit and trial, we can deduce that n = 3 years.

3.10.2.3 Population Compounding

The concept of compounding can be applied to calculate the population compounding at a certain rate.

Example 5: If the population of a town increases at 6% p.a., but decreases due to emigration by 1% p.a., what is the net percentage increase in the population in 3 years?

$\Rightarrow$ Say the population before the increase is P_0 and after 3 years is P_3

So, $P_n = P_0 \left(1 \pm \dfrac{r}{100}\right)^n$

$P_3 = 100 \left(1 + \dfrac{(6-1)}{100}\right)^3 = 100 \left(1 + \dfrac{1}{20}\right)^3 = 100 \left(\dfrac{21}{20}\right)^3 = 100 \times 2.1 \times 2.1 \times 2.1 = 115.76$;
net increase in population = r = Growth rate – Emigration rate = 6 – 1 = 5%

So, the net % increase = 115.76 – 100 = 15.76%.

Different rates of compounding for different periods:

So far we have seen that there is one rate of compounding for the whole period. However, there can be two or three different rates for different periods. Let us see how.

Example 6: If the population of a town increases at 5% for the first 2 years, increases at 2% for the next 3 years, and then decreases at 2% for the next 2 years, what is the net percentage increase in population in 7 years?

The formula of compounding can be modified as:

$P_n = P_0 \left(1 \pm \dfrac{r_1}{100}\right)^{n_1} \left(1 \pm \dfrac{r_2}{100}\right)^{n_2} \left(1 \pm \dfrac{r_3}{100}\right)^{n_3}$;

where n_1, n_2, n_3 are the time periods, $n = n_1 + n_2 + n_3$; and r_1, r_2, r_3 are the rates for respective time periods.

$$P_7 = 100\left(1 + \frac{5}{100}\right)^3\left(1 + \frac{2}{100}\right)^3\left(1 - \frac{2}{100}\right)^2 = 100\left(\frac{21}{20}\right)^2\left(\frac{51}{50}\right)^3\left(\frac{49}{50}\right)^2 = 112.3$$

So, the net % increase = 112.37 – 100 = 12.37%.

3.11   Expressions

Any form of numeric representation representing a number is called an **Expression.**

Example: $-3, (x - 2y), \frac{2p-3q^3}{9}, \sqrt[3]{\frac{y^6}{2-y^2}}$. All these expressions including -3 show numbers. When we plug in or key in the value of variables x, y, p, q in the expressions, we get their numeric values.

An expression does not contain '=' sign. If two expressions are equated by '=' sign, it is called an **Equation**; however if they are separated by either of $<, >, \geq, \leq$ signs, it is called an **Inequation** or **Inequality.**

Simplification of expressions:

Combining like terms: $(2x + 3x)$ is an expression in a distributive or an expanded form. We can simplify the expression by adding like terms. So, the simplified form is: $(2x + 3x) = 5x$.

Expanded form of expression	Simplified form of expression	Comments
$2x^2 + 3x - 4x - 4$	$2x^2 - x - 4$	$3x$ and $-4x$ are like terms, and $2x^2$ and 4 unlike terms.
$(3x - 4) - (4y - 4)$	$3x - 4 - 4y + 4$ $= (3x - 4y)$	$3x$ and $-4y$ are not like terms. Apple would be added to apple & not to orange.
$2x^2 + 3\sqrt{x^4} - 4x$	$2x^2 + 3\sqrt{x^4} - 4x$ $= 2x^2 + 3x^2 - 4x$ $= 5x^2 - 4x$	Simplify the exponents.
$\frac{2x}{y} - \frac{x}{y}$	$= \frac{x}{y}$	Consider $\frac{x}{y}$ as one variable.
$4x^2y - 10xy^2$	$4x^2y - 10xy^2$ $= 2xy(2x - 5y)$	Take out common factor. Depending on the situation you may have to either expand an expression or simplify it.

3.12 Equations

Equality of two expressions is called Equation.

Example: $2x + 3 = 0$ is an equation.

Here there are two expressions: '$2x + 3$' and '0'. An equation has two sides: Left had side ($2x + 3$) and right hand side (0). The left had side (LHS) always equals the right hand side (RHS).

Manipulating an equation:

A. Whatever you do to any side of an equation, do the same to the other side:

Say the equation is $2x + 3 = 0$ and we are interested in deducing the value of the variable x.

To get the value of x, we must try to isolate x on either side of the equation. Here x accompanies a co-efficient '2', and a number, 3, added to it. So, we must get rid of '3' and '2'. Let us see how.

$2x + 3 = 0$

$\Rightarrow 2x + 3 - 3 = 0 - 3$; Subtracting '3' from both the sides: LHS and RHS

$\Rightarrow 2x = -3$;

$\Rightarrow \frac{2x}{2} = -\frac{3}{2}$; Dividing both the sides by '2' to get rid of x's co-efficient '2'

$\boldsymbol{x = -\frac{3}{2}}$; We finally get the value of x.

Example 1: Find the value of x for the equation: $\frac{3x-7}{5} = 7$.

$\frac{3x-7}{5} = 7$

$\Rightarrow \frac{3x-7}{5} \times 5 = 7 \times 5$; Multiplying both the sides by '5' to get rid of '5' in the denominator

$\Rightarrow 3x - 7 = 35$;

$\Rightarrow 3x - 7 + 7 = 35 + 7$; Adding '7' on both the sides to get rid of '-7' from LHS
$3x = 42$;

$\Rightarrow \frac{3x}{3} = \frac{42}{3}$; Dividing both the sides by '3' to get rid of x's co-efficient '3'

$\boldsymbol{x = 14}$

B. Transposition:

The above method of manipulation is time-consuming. Let us see another method to get the same result: **Transposition.**

We take the same equation: $2x + 3 = 0$. We can transpose '3' from LHS to RHS.

"If any expression on any side is positive, it will be transposed as negative on the other side and vice-versa."

$2x + 3 = 0$
=> $2x = -3$; '+3' is transposed from LHS to RHS as '-3'; Note the sign change!

$x = -\frac{3}{2}$; Co-efficient '2' transposed from LHS to RHS as '$\frac{1}{2}$'; Note no sign change

Example 2: Find the value of x for the equation: $\frac{3x-7}{5} = 7$.

=> $\frac{3x-7}{5} = 7$
$3x - 7 = 7 \times 5$; Cross-multiplication of '5'. Since '5' was on the denominator of the LHS, it will go to RHS as multiplicand. Remember no sign change.

$3x - 7 = 35$;
$3x = 35 + 7$; '-7' is transposed from LHS to RHS as '+7'; Remember sign change
$3x = 42$;
$x = \frac{42}{3}$; Co-efficient '3' transposed from LHS to RHS as '$\frac{1}{3}$'; Remember no sign change

$x = 14$

Example 3: Find the value of x for the equation: $7\left(\frac{x}{2} + 3\right) = 21$

=> $7\left(\frac{x}{2} + 3\right) = 21$
$\frac{x}{2} + 3 = \frac{21}{7}$; Multiplicand '7' transposed from LHS to RHS as '$\frac{1}{7}$'; Remember no sign change

$\frac{x}{2} + 3 = 3$

$\frac{x}{2} = 3 - 3$; '+3' is transposed from LHS to RHS as '-3'; Remember sign change

$\frac{x}{2} = 0$;

$x = 0 \times 2$; Cross-multiplication of '2'. Since '2' was on the denominator of the LHS, it will go to RHS as multiplicand. Remember no sign change

$x = 0$

Example 4: Find the value of x for the equation: $3\left(\sqrt{x^2 + 3}\right) = 9$.

=> $3\left(\sqrt{x^2 + 3}\right) = 9$
$\sqrt{x^2 + 3} = \frac{9}{3}$ => $\sqrt{x^2 + 3} = 3$; Transposing '3'.

$=> (\sqrt{x^2+3})^2 = 3^2 => x^2 + 3 = 9$; Squaring both the sides to get rid of square-root
$=> x^2 = 9 - 3 => x^2 = 6$; Transposing '3'.

$x^2 = 6$;
$=> \sqrt{x^2} = \sqrt{6}$; taking square-root of both the sides to get rid of square.

$\boldsymbol{x = \pm\sqrt{6}}$

Example 5: Find the value of x for the equation: $\dfrac{3(x-2) + 2(3x-2)}{x-5} = -2.$

$=> \dfrac{3(x-2) + 2(3x-2)}{x-5} = -2$

$=> 3x - 2 + 2(3x - 2) = -2(x - 5)$; Cross-multiplication
$=> 3x - 6 + 6x - 4 = -2x + 10$; Expansion
$=> 3x + 6x + 2x = 6 + 4 + 10$; Transposing like terms and isolating x
$=> 11x = 20$; Adding like terms

$\text{X} = \dfrac{20}{11}$

3.12.1   System of Equations

So far we have dealt with one variable and one equation. If we have two or more equations, we call them **System of Equations**. You can get the unique value of the variable, say x from one equation; however if you have to deal with more than two variables, you have to deal with more than two equations.

Say an equation is $2x + 3y = 13$. Since there are two variables, x and y, we need two equations to get their unique values. Say another equation is $2x - 3y = -5$.

So, we have a system of equations: $2x + 3y = 13$ and $2x - 3y = -5$. There are quite a few methods of solving the system of equations; we discuss two of them.

'System of equations' is also referred to as **'Simultaneous Equations'**.

Linear equation:

When the exponent or the power of variable(s) in an equation is '1', it is called a linear equation. $2x + 3y = 13$ and $2x - 3y = -5$ are linear equation.

The standard form of simultaneous equations is $ax + by = c$; where x and y are the coefficients of the variables x and y respectively and c is a constant term.

Solving simultaneous equations:

1. Method of Elimination:

In this method, we eliminate one of the variable using both the equations and get the numeric value of other variable.

By plugging in the numeric value of the other variable in any equation, we get numeric value of the first variable. Follow the following steps to solve the equations.

Step 1: Simplify and transform both the equations in the form $ax + by = c$, if needed

=> The two equations ($2x + 3y = 13$ and $2x - 3y = -5$), we are dealing with are already in the standard form.

Step 2: Decide which variable should be eliminated

=> If you are interested in finding the value of x, then eliminate y, and vice-versa; however, if you need to calculate the values of both the variables, decide which variable is relatively easier to eliminate.

=> If the co-efficients of one of the two variables are same in the equations, you should eliminate that variable; however, if the co-efficients are not same, you may still decide which variable should be eliminated; it depends on how easy it is for you to make the absolute value of the co-efficients of a variable equal. This part can be better understood in step 3.

> For our set of equations: $2x + 3y = 13$ and $2x - 3y = -5$, we have to find out the values of both x and y. We decide that we will eliminate variable y as the coefficients of y for the equations are equal and are of opposite sign. This part can be better understood in step 4.

Step 3: Make the co-efficients of the variable to be eliminated equal

=> If the co-efficients of the variable to be eliminated are not same in both the equations, you should make them equal by multiplying with minimum possible numbers to the co-efficient(s).

> For our set of equations: $2x + 3y = 13$ and $2x - 3y = -5$, we have already decided that we will eliminate variable y, since the absolute value of the co-efficients of y in both the equations are equal ('3'), we need not multiply equation(s) with a number(s) to make co-efficients equal.

Step 3: Add or subtract the equations

=> If the signs of the co-efficients of the variable to be eliminated are same, add the equations, else subtract.

> For our set of equations: $2x + 3y = 13$ and $2x - 3y = -5$, since the signs of the co-efficients of y in both the equations are same ($-$), we should add the equations.

> $2x + 3y = 13$ ————————(1); name it eqn. (1)
> $2x - 3y = -5$ ————————(2); name it eqn. (2)
> ————————
> $4x = 8$; $+3y$ and $-3y$ get cancelled.

> $x = 8/4 \Rightarrow x = 2$.

Step 4: Calculate the value of other variable

=> Substitute the value of the variable derived in step 3 in any of the equations convenient to you.

> Let us plug in the value of $x = 2$ in the eqn (1), and we get:

$2.2 + 3y = 13 => 3y = 13 - 4 = 9 => 3y = 9 => y = \frac{9}{3}$

$=> y = 3.$

So, $x = 2$, and $y = 3$.

Step 5 (Optional): Cross check the values derived by plugging in both the equation

=> Plug in the values of both the variables in both the equations; LHS and RHS must be equal.

Eqn(1): $2x + 3y = 13 => 2(2) + 3(3) = 13 => 4 + 9 = 13 => \mathbf{13 = 13}.$

Eqn(2): $2x - 3y = -5 => 2(2) - 3(3) = -5 => 4 - 9 = -5 => \mathbf{-5 = -5}.$

This proves that the values derived are correct.

Example 1: Find out the values of x and y for the equations $3x + 5y - 21 = 0$ and $2x + 3y = 13$.

=> Make the equation $3x + 5y - 21 = 0$ in the standard form: $3x+5y = 21$. Second equation $2x + 3y = 13$ is already in standard form.

=> So the equations are:

$3x + 5y = 21$—————-(1)
$2x + 3y = 13$—————-(2); name the equations

=> Since we have to find out the values of both the variables x and y, it is immaterial to choose which variable should be eliminated; however looking at the equations, we decide that we will eliminate x.

=> Next task is to make the co-efficients of x in both the equations equal.

By multiplying '2' to the eqn(1), and '3' to the eqn(2), we get,

$2 \times (3x + 5y = 21)$ ————-(1)
$3 \times (2x + 3y = 13)$ ———--(2);

$=> 6x + 10y = 42$———-(1)
$=> 6x + 9y\ \ = 39$———-(2);

=>Since the signs of the co-efficients of x for both the equations are same, we will subtract eqn (2) from eqn (1).

$6x + 10y = 42$————–(1)

$6x + 9y = 39$————–(2);
$-$ $-$ $-$

———————————————————————————
————–- When we subtract eqn (2) from eqn (1), the signs of the co-efficients and the constant of eqn (2) will change (+ will turn − and vice-versa)

=> After cancellation of $6x$, we get $10y - 9y = 42 - 39 =>$ $y = 3$.

=> Now, plug in the value of y in any equation; we choose eqn (2)
$2x + 3y = 13 => 2x + 3.3 = 13 => 2x + 9 = 13 => 2x = 13 - 9 => 2x = 4$

=> $x = 2$.

So, we get $x = 2$, and $y = 3$.

2. Method of Substitution:

In this method, by choosing an equation we calculate the value of a variable in terms of other variable and constant, plug in that variable's value in the second equation, and get the numeric value of the other variable.

Again, by plugging in the numeric value of the other variable in any equation, we get the numeric value of the first variable. Follow the following steps to solve the equations.

Step 1: Decide which variable should be substituted

=> We will deal with the two equations ($x + 3y = 11$ and $2x - 3y = -5$).
=> Observe which variable in an equation does not have its co-efficient; that very variable should be chosen to be substituted; the reason for choosing that variable is that though its value would be in terms of the other variable and the constant, it would not have any denominator to deal with.

On this basis, we choose eqn (1): $x + 3y = 11$, and variable x to be substituted in eqn (2): $2x - 3y = -5$

Step 2: Calculate the value of the chosen variable in terms of the other variable and constant

$x + 3y = 11 =>$ $x = 11 - 3y$———— say equation (1)

Step 3: Substitute the value calculated in step 2 in the other equation

By plugging in the value of $x = 11 - 3y$ in the eqn (2): $2x - 3y = -5$, we get,

$2.(11 - 3y) - 3y = -5 \implies 22 - 6y - 3y = -5 \implies -9y = -5 - 22 \implies$
$-9y = -27 \implies y = -27 - 9$

$\implies y = 3.$

Step 4: Calculate the value of other variable

Substitute the value of the variable derived in step 3 in any of the equation convenient to you, preferably equation (1).

Let us plug in the value of $y = 3$ in the eqn: $x = 11 - 3y$, and we get:

$x = 11 - 3.3 \implies x = 11 - 9 \implies x = 2.$

So, $x = 2$, and $y = 3$.

Example 2: Find out the values of x, & y from the equations: $3x + 5y - 21 = 0$ and $2x + 3y = 13$.

$\implies$ No variable in any equation is without co-efficient, so you may choose any variable and any equation to start with.

$\implies$ Say we chose eqn (2) and variable x

So, $2x + 3y = 13 \implies 2x = 13 - 3y \implies x = \frac{13-3y}{2}$

$\implies$ By plugging in the value of $x = \frac{13-3y}{2}$ in eqn(1): $3x + 5y - 21 = 0$, we get,

$3.\left(\dfrac{13 - 3y}{2}\right) + 5y - 21 = 0 \implies \dfrac{3(13 - 3y) + 2 \times 5y - 2 \times 21}{2} = 0$

$3(13 - 3y) + 2 \times 5y - 2 \times 21 = 2 \times 0 \implies 39 - 9y + 10y - 42 = 0 \implies y - 3 = 0 \implies y = 3.$

$\implies$ By plugging in the value of $y = 3$ in eqn: $x = \frac{13-3y}{2}$, we get

$x = \dfrac{13 - 3.(3)}{2} = \dfrac{13 - 9}{2} = \dfrac{4}{2} \implies x = 2.$

So, $x = 2$, and $y = 3$.

Number of solutions

For a linear equation: $2x + 3y = 12$, we cannot find out the unique solution or the unique values of the variables x and y; however we can find out infinite number of consistent solutions. Say $x = 3$, then $y = 2$. Following illustration shows few consistent solutions.

Equation: $2x + 3y = 12$

x	0	6	1	–1	3	2
y	4	0	10/3	14/3	2	8/3

For integer only solutions, we can follow the following method:

Find out one possible integer solution for the equation $2x + 3y = 12$: it is obvious that it is $x = 6$ and $y = 0$.

To get the next value of x, subtract the coefficient of y (with sign) from the value of x obtained and to get the next value of x, add the coefficient of x (with sign) to the value of y obtained previously. Thus gives us $x = 6 - 3 = 3$ and $y = 0 + 2 = 2$.

Alternatively, to get the next value of x, add the coefficient of y (with sign) to the value of x obtained and to get the next value of y, subtract the coefficient of x (with sign) from the value of y obtained previously. Thus gives us $x = 6+3 = 9$ and $y = 0-2 = -2$.

The above steps can be continued indefinitely to get all sets of values of integer values of x and y.

If only positive values are needed, we continue the process only till when the values of the variables remain positive.

Please remember that the above method is only applicable for two variables.

Unique vs. Consistent solution:

Let us see the following system of equations:

$2x + 3y = 12$————–(1); &
$4x + 6y = 24$————–(2)

You would have observed that eqn (2) is derived from the parent eqn (1) by multiplying itself by '2', so in fact both the equations are the same. So, though these equations are **consistent**, they would **not have unique solution** rather **infinite number of solutions.**

Let us see the following system of equation:

$2x + 3y = 12$————–(1); &
$4x + 6y = 4$ ————–(2)

You would have observed that eqn (2) is derived from the parent eqn (1) by multiplying itself by '2' to its LHS, but its RHS is something different, other than anticipated '24', so the given equations are **inconsistent.** They **would not have any solution** at all.

Let us see the following system of equations:

$4x + 6y = 24$ ————-(1); &
$3x + 2y = 13$ ————-(2)

You would have observed that eqn (2) is different from the parent eqn (1), and you cannot derive eqn (2) by manipulating eqn (1), so these equations given are **consistent,** and **would have unique solution.**

In a nut shell for the system of equation:

$a_1x + b_1y = c_1$ ————-(1);&
$a_2x + b_2y = c_2$ ————-(2)

Following table illustrates the nature of equations and number of solutions.

$a_1x + b_1y = c_1$ ————-(1); &
$a_2x + b_2y = c_2$ ————-(2)

Ratio of co-efficients and constant	Nature of equation	Number number of solution(s)
$\dfrac{a_1}{a_2} = \dfrac{b_1}{b_2} = \dfrac{c_1}{c_2}$	Consistent equations	Infinite of solutions
$\dfrac{a_1}{a_2} = \dfrac{b_1}{b_2} \neq \dfrac{c_1}{c_2}$	Inconsistent equations	No solution
$\dfrac{a_1}{a_2} \neq \dfrac{b_1}{b_2}$	Consistent equations	Unique solution

There may be two identical equations which may seem to look unique equations, for example:

$2x + 3y = 12$ ————-(1); &

$\dfrac{x + \frac{3}{2}y}{6} = 1$ ————-(2).

If you did not pay attention to this, you may fall in the trap laid by the test-maker, and without solving the equations, you may decide that the two equations will render unique values of x and y.

3.12.2 Quadratic Equation

A linear equation has variable(s) which have the exponent or power of '1'; whereas a **Quadratic Equation** comprises of at least one variable(s) which have the exponent or power of '2'. The name Quadratic comes from "Quad" meaning "Square", as the variable(s) get squared.

Standard form of a quadratic equation is: $ax^2 + bx + c = 0$, where $a \neq 0$. There are at the most two values of x, satisfying the equation; these values are also called **Roots** of the equation.

Methods of calculating roots:

1. Factoring quadratic equation:

Say a quadratic equation is: $2x^2 + 10x + 12 = 0$. Values: $x = -2$ and $x = -3$ satisfy the equation, so $x = -2$ and $x = -3$ are the roots of the equation.

We will find out the roots of the equation through factoring method.

Step 1: Manipulate the equation to make it in standard form: $ax^2 + bx + c = 0$

=> Our eqn is $2x^2 + 10x + 12 = 0$. We simplify the equation by dividing it by '2', so we get $x^2 + 5x + 6 = 0$. Here $a = 1, b = 5$, and $c = 6$.

Step 2: Split "ac"

=> Calculate the product of a and c.

=> For our eqn: $\boldsymbol{ac = 1 \times 6 \Rightarrow ac = 6}$.

=> Mentally run through the factors of the $\boldsymbol{ac}$, and choose any two of them, such that their sum equals **'co-efficient of $\boldsymbol{x}$: $\boldsymbol{b}$'**.

=> In our equation: $x^2 + 5x + 6 = 0$, 'co-efficient of $x : b = 5$', and $ac = 6$. Factors of '6' are {1, 2, 3, 6}.

There are two possible pairs of factors that make their product equal to $6 : 1 \times 6 = 6$, and $2 \times 3 = 6$; but out of these two pairs, we must choose {2, 3} as their sum also makes co-efficient of $x : b = 5 : 2 + 3 = 5$).

So the equation can be rewritten as: $x^2 + 2x + 3x + 6 = 0$.

We can pair first two terms and last two terms as: $x(x + 2) + 3(x + 2) = 0$. Here we can pull out $(x + 2)$ as common, so the equation becomes the product of two factors:

$(x + 2)(x + 3) = 0.$

We know that if the product of two expression is '0', at least one of the expressions must be '0'; so, either $x + 2 = 0$ or $x + 3 = 0$. This gives either $x = -2$ or -3. There are the two roots or the solution of the equation.

2. Using formula:

Roots of the equation: $ax^2 + bx + c = 0$ are given by:

$$x_1 = \frac{-b + \sqrt{b^2 - 4ac}}{2a}; \, \&$$

$$x_2 = \frac{-b - \sqrt{b^2 - 4ac}}{2a}; \text{ where } b^2 - 4ac \text{ is called discriminant } (\Delta)$$

The equation $2x^2 - 2x - 12 = 0$ can be simplified as $x^2 - x - 6 = 0$; where $a = 1, b = -1,$ and $x = -6$. The roots are referred to as $x_1, \& x_2$.

$$x_1 \, \& \, x_2 = \frac{-b \pm \sqrt{b^2 - 4ac}}{2a} = \frac{-(-1) \pm \sqrt{(-1)^2 - (4.1. -6}}{2.1} = \frac{1 \pm \sqrt{1 - 24}}{2} = \frac{1 \pm 5}{2}$$

$$x_1 = \frac{1 + 5}{2} = 3, \text{ or } x_2 = \frac{1 - 5}{2} = 3 = -2; \text{ so } x_1 = -2 \text{ and } x_2 = -3$$

The term discriminant $(\Delta) = b^2 - 4ac$ can be positive/Negative/Zero, depending on the values of $a, b,$ and c.

The following table illustrates the relationship between $\Delta = b^2 - 4ac$, and two roots of the equation.

$\Delta = b^2 - 4ac$	Nature of roots	Form/Value or Example
Positive (> 0)	Real & Unequal; Two distinct roots	$x_1 \, \& \, x_2 = \dfrac{-b \pm \sqrt{b^2 - 4ac}}{2a}$
	If Δ is perfect square, roots are Rational	For $x^2 + 5x + 6 = 0$; $x = -2$, or $= -3$
	If Δ is not a perfect square, roots are Irrational	For $x^2 + 2x - 6 = 0$; $x_1 = (-1 + \sqrt{7})$, $x_2 = (-1 - \sqrt{7})$
Equal (=)	Real; only one root	$-\dfrac{b}{2a}$; For $x^2 + 4x + 4 = 0; x = 2$
Negative (< 0)	Imaginary roots	$a + ib$; For $x^2 + 2x + 6 = 0$, $x_1 = (-1 + \sqrt{-5})$, $x_2 = (-1 - \sqrt{-5})$

3.12.2.1 Roots of quadratic equation

So far we have seen how we can find out the roots of the quadratic equation. There may be instances in which you have to form a quadratic equation if the values of roots are given. Let us see how we can do it.

We have seen that the factors of $x^2 + 5x + 6 = 0$ are $(x + 2)$ and $(x + 3)$; where the roots are: $x = -2$ or $x = -3$. So, we can write the equation as $[x - (-2)][x - (-3)] = 0$ or $(x - x_1)(x - x_2) = 0$.

If you expand $(x - x_1)(x - x_2) = 0$, you will get $x^2 - (x_1 + x_2) + x_1x_2 = 0$; where $x_1 + x_2$ = sum of roots, and x_1x_2 = product of roots.

$$x^2 - \textbf{(Sum of Roots)}x + \textbf{(Product of Roots)} = 0$$

Let us call it **Normal form** of quadratic equation. Here **co-efficient of x** is the **middle term: '$-$ Sum of roots'** and the **constant** is the **last term: 'Product of roots'.**

Standard form of equation: $ax^2 + by^2 + c = 0$ can be written as $x^2 + \left(\frac{b}{a}\right) + \left(\frac{c}{a}\right) = 0$

$=> x^2 - \left(-\frac{b}{a}\right) + \left(\frac{c}{a}\right) = 0$. So, here **Sum of roots** $= -\frac{b}{a}$ and **Product of roots** $= \frac{c}{a}$.

Example 1: Two roots of a quadratic equation are $-\frac{1}{2}$ and $\frac{3}{2}$. Find out the equation.

Sum of the roots $= -\frac{1}{2} + \frac{3}{2} = 1$, and product of roots $= -\frac{1}{2} \times \frac{3}{2} = -\frac{3}{4}$
$=>$ So, the equation is: $x^2 - (1)x + \left(-\frac{3}{4}\right) = 0$;
$=> x^2 - x - \frac{3}{4} = 0$
$=> \textbf{4}x^2 - \textbf{4}x - \textbf{3} = \textbf{0}$

Example 2: One of the roots of a quadratic equation is 2 and the product of roots is 6. Find out the equation.

Product of roots $= x_1x_2 = 2.x_2 = 6$. So, $x_2 = 3$;
$=>$ Now, Sum of the roots $= 2 + 3 = 5$;
$=>$ So, the equation is: $x^2 - (\text{Sum of roots})x + (\text{Product of roots}) = 0$.
$=> \textbf{x}^2 - \textbf{5}x + \textbf{6} = \textbf{0}$

Example 3: For a quadratic equation: $2x^2 - 4x = 3$, find out the sum of roots, and product of roots.

The equation can be written in standard form as: $2x^2 - 4x - 3 = 0$
$=>$ The normal form requires that the co-efficient of x^2 must be '1' so, we divide the equation by '2', and we $x^2 - 2x - \frac{3}{2} = 0$
$=>$ The co-efficient of $x = -2$; so the sum of roots $= 2$, and the constant $= -\frac{3}{2}$; so the product of roots $= -\frac{3}{2}$.

3.12.2.2 Higher order equations

Though higher order equations/polynomial equations are out of scope of the GRE, there may an equation such as this: $x^3 - 5x^2 + 6x = 0$ which is a not a quadratic equation; however you can still solve the equation in a quadratic equation way. Let us see how.

$x^3 - 5x^2 + 6x = 0$;
$\Rightarrow x(x^2 - 5x + 6) = 0$
$\Rightarrow x(x - 2)(x - 3) = 0$
$\Rightarrow$ Either $x = 0$ or $x - 2 = 0$ or $x - 3 = 0 \Rightarrow x = 0$ or 2 or 3. So there are three roots of the equation.

Never divide the equation by x if you are not sure that $x \neq 0$. Not understanding this concept may land you in trouble. See the following equation.

$x^3 - 4x^2 + 4x = 0$;
$\Rightarrow x(x^2 - 4x + 4) = 0 \Rightarrow$ Dividing the equation by x, we get $x^2 - 4x + 4 = 0$
$\Rightarrow (x - 2)^2 = 0 \Rightarrow x = 2$, a unique value of x! Right! No it's wrong.

We have missed out $x = 0$; so there are two possible values of x : 0 and 2.

3.13 Absolute numbers

We know that any real number can either be 0, positive or negative. When we ignore the negative sign of a number, we seem to be interested in its absolute value and not in its direction of value.

In other words, absolute value of a number is its distance from '0'. If a number is presented between two-vertical bar (pipe ‖) symbol, it means we are interested in its absolute value.

Say, a number is x, then its absolute value is $|x|$, as depicted in the figure below.

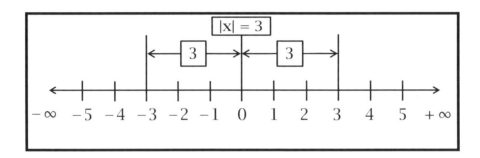

So, we can say that $|\pm x| = x$.

Key properties:

(1) $\sqrt{x^2} = |x|$

(2) $|\pm x| = x$

(3) $|x| = |-x|; -|x| \neq |-x|$

(4) $|x| \geq 0$

(5) $|x \pm y| = |y \pm x|$

> Say $x = 10$ and $y = -10$, then
> $|x - y| = |10 - (-10)| = |10 + 10| = 20$;
> $|y - x| = |-10 - 10| = |-20| = 20$.

(6) $|x + y| \leq |x| + |y|$

> Say $x = 10$ and $y = 10$, then
> $|x + y| = |10 + 10| = 20$;
> $|x| + |y| = |10| + |10| = 10 + 10 = 20$, hence $|x + y| = |x| + |y|$

But, say $x = 10$ and $y = -10$, then

$|x + y| = |10 + (-10)| = |10 - 10| = 0$;

$|x| + |y| = |10| + |-10| = 10 + 10 = 20$, hence $|x + y| < |x| + |y|$

This deduction is an important finding and is tested by test-makers especially in DS questions.

Remember that the equality holds true only when both x and y are of the same sign and the inequality holds true when x and y are of opposite signs.

(7) $|x - y| \geq |x| - |y|$

(8) $|x \times y| = |y \times x| = |x| \times |y| = |y| \times |x|$

(9) $|x \div y| = |x| \div |y|$

Example: If $7|2x - 3| = 21$, what is the value of x?

Simplify $7|2x - 3| = 21$ by dividing both the sides by '3'; we get $|2x - 3| = 3$.

=> $2x - 3 = 3$ or $-(2x - 3) = 3$.

=> $2x - 3 = 3$ => $2x = 6$ => $x = 3$; and

=> $-(2x - 3) = 3$ => $-2x + 3 = 3$ => $-2x = 0$ => $x = 0$.

So $x = 0$ or 3.

3.13.1 Inequality

To understand Inequality, first understand Equality.

$x = 5$ means that the value of the variable x equals 5.

The inequality could be anything $x \neq 4$, $x < 6$ or $x > 4$.

When the two sides of an expression are not equal, it is called Inequality. Inequalities use symbols $<, >, \leq,$ or $\geq$ to describe the relationship between two expressions, for example: $10 < 12, 12 > 8, x \leq 4, x + 2y \geq 4$ etc.

Understanding inequality:

Inequality	Meaning	Example
$x < 5$	x is less than 5	x can be any value less than 5 on number line. It can be 0, 1, –155, or any other value up to negative infinity. Do not assume that x is an integer. x can even be 4.999. Always consider that x is a real number until stated that it is an integer.
$y > 10$	y is greater than 10	y can be any value greater than 10 on number scale. It can be 10.0001, 10.56, 11, or any other value up to infinity.
$p \leq 10$	p is less than or equal to 10	p can be any value less than or equal to 10 on number line. It can be 10, 4, -2.3, or any other value up to negative infinity.
$q \geq 10$	q is greater than or equal to 10	q can be any value greater than or equal to 10 on number line. It can be 10, 14, 23.5, or any other value up to infinity.
$-2 \leq x < 4$; x is an integer	x is greater than or equal to -2 but less than 4	$x = \{-2, -1, 0, 1, 2, 3\}$
$-2 > x \geq -4$; x is an integer	x is less than -2 and greater than or equal to -4	$x = \{-3, -4\}$

Representation of inequalities on number line:

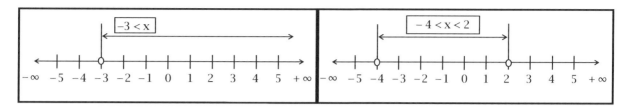

Key properties of Inequalities:

(1) You can **add or subtract anything from an inequality**.

Say, $x + 3 > 10$.

You can subtract 3 from both the sides, so the inequality becomes, $x + 3 - 3 > 10 - 3 => x > 7$.

Take another example; say, $y - 3 > -10$.

You can add 3 on both the sides, so the inequality becomes, $y - 3 + 3 > -10 + 3 => y > -7$.

(2) You can multiply or divide an inequality by a **positive** number.

Say, $2x > 10$.

You can divide the inequality by 2, so the inequality becomes, $\frac{2x}{2} > \frac{10}{2} => x > 5$.

Say, $\frac{y}{3} > -10$. You can multiply the inequality by 3, so the inequality becomes, $\frac{y}{3} \times 3 > -10 \times 3 => y > -30$.

(3) You can multiply or divide an inequality by a **negative** number, but doing so will ask for **reversing** the sign of inequality.

We know that $7 > 5$;

if we multiply an inequality by –1, it will become $-7 > -5$ which is wrong to say because $-7 < -5$; so when we multiply or divide an inequality with a negative number, we have to flip the sign.

Say, $-2x > 10$.

You can divide the inequality by –2, so the inequality becomes,

$$\frac{-2x}{-2} \not< \frac{10}{-2} => x < -5.$$

Say, $\frac{-y}{3} > -10$. You can multiply the inequality by –3, so the inequality becomes,

$$\frac{-y}{3} \times -3 \not< -10 \times -3 => y < 30.$$

3.13.2 Inequalities with absolute numbers

Few tough questions may be asked combining inequalities and absolute numbers.

Example 1: If $|x + 1| \leq 4$, what is x?

$|x + 1| \leq 4$

$=>$ If $x + 1 \leq 4$ or $-(x + 1) \leq 4$

$x + 1 \leq 4 => x \leq 3$

Or, $-(x + 1) \leq 4 => x + 1 \geq 4 => x \geq -5$. (Pay attention to reversal of sign of inequality)

So, $3 \geq x \geq -5$

It can be represented graphically as below.

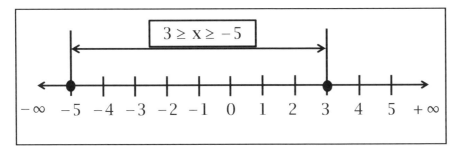

Example 2: If $|2x + 1| \geq 3$, what is x?

$|2x + 1| \geq 3 => 2x + 1 \geq 3$ or $-(2x + 1) \geq 3$

If $2x + 1 \geq 3 => 2x \geq 2 => x \geq 1$

Or, $-(2x + 1) \geq 3 => 2x + 1 \leq -3 => 2x \leq -4 => x \leq -2$. (Pay attention to reversal of sign of inequality)

So $-2 \geq x$ or $x \geq 1$

It can be represented graphically as below.

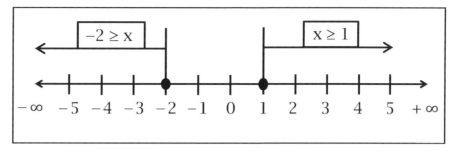

Example 3: If $8 + x^2 \geq 12$, what is the rage of x?

$8 + x^2 \geq 12$

$=> x^2 \geq 4;$

taking square root of both the sides, we get,

$|x| \geq 2 => x \geq 2$ or $x \leq -2.$

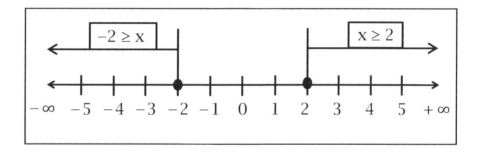

3.13.3 Compound Inequality

An inequality that has more than one inequality symbol in an expression is called compound inequality. $2 > x \geq 4$ is an example of compound inequality. GRE inequality questions may involve more than one inequality. To solve such questions, you may have to transform several inequalities to a compound inequality.

Example 4: If $x > 4, x \leq 10$, and $x < 12$, what is the range of x?

Step 1: Fix 'more than x' or 'more than or equal to x' inequality.

There is only one 'more than x' inequality, so we fix $x > 4$.

Step 2: Fix 'less than x' or 'less than or equal to x' inequality.

There is one 'less than x' and one 'less than or equal to x' inequalities, but between the two inequalities $x \leq 10$, and $x < 12$, we choose the first one i.e. $x \leq 10$ since $x \leq 10$ is a subset of $x < 12$, not vice-versa; so we fix $x \leq 10$.

Step 3: Combine both the inequalities derived in steps 1 and 2.

Finally, we get $4 < x \le 10$.

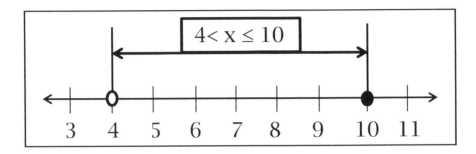

Note that:

If $x > y$, and $y > z$, then we can combine the inequalities as $x > y > z$ or $x > z$.

However,

If $x > y$, and $y < z$, then though we can combine the inequalities as $x > y < z$, but we **cannot** deduce that $x > z$.

3.13.4 Mathematical operations on inequalities

(1) **Addition and subtraction:**

If $x > y$ and $a < b$, we cannot deduce that $x + a < y + b$; it is wrong.

We must make both the inequalities in the same direction. So, we can rewrite the inequalities as $x > y$ and $b > a$, and now we can add these.

So, $x + b > y + a$.

Let's take another example.

If $x - 3 < y \le x + 6$, then we **cannot** write the inequality as $x < y \le x + 6 + 3 =>$ $x < y \le x + 9$. It is wrong!

If you subtract a number from one part of a compound inequality, you must subtract the same number from all the parts.

The simplified and corrected inequality is: $x < y + 3 \leq x + 9$.

(2) **Multiplication and division:**

If $x < -\frac{y}{3} \leq 3x$, then we can simplify the inequality by multiplying it by –3.

So, $-3\left(x < -\frac{y}{3} \leq 3x\right) \Rightarrow -3x > (-\frac{y}{3} \times -3) \geq -3 \times 3x \Rightarrow -3x > y \geq -9x$.

Always be wary of changing the sign of inequality when multiplying or dividing it by a negative number.

The inequality can also be written as $3x < -y \leq 9x$.

Similarly, if $3x > 6y - 3 > 6z$, we can divide the inequality by 3, so we get $x > 2y - 1 > 2z$. Always remember that each part of the compound inequality should be divided.

3.14 Functions

We all know that area of a square equals square of its sides; $A = a^2$.

It is clear that when we feed the value of the side of square, a, in the expression, we get the value of area, A. Here, 'a' is called an **Independent variable** because 'a' may have any value, it is not dependent on the value 'A'; whereas, 'A' is called a **Dependent variable** because 'A' cannot assume any value on its own, it is always dependent on the value 'a'.

So, **Function** is a relationship between two variables—one of them is called is an **Independent variable** and the other one is called **Dependent variable**—such that for one value of independent variable, there is only one value of dependent variable.

In other words, 'a' is an **Input**, and 'A' is an **Output**; the expression which can also be called a **Function**, expresses a relationship between the two variables.

For the formula $A = a^2$, we can write that $A = f(a)$.

Similarly, if we write $y = f(x)$, it means that x is an **independent variable**, and y is a **dependent variable**.

The significance of writing 'f' is to show the relationship between the two variables. It can also be written as $y = g(x)$ or $y = h(x)$. Here 'f', 'g', and 'h' are neither variables nor constants. You must NOT infer that in the expression $y = f(x)$, 'f' and 'x' are multiplied.

There would be only one independent variable and only one dependent variable in quant questions.

Let us see couple of terminologies associated with function:

1. Domain:

Set of values, an independent variable can take is called Domain. For the above function $A = f(a)$, the domain of 'a' is all positive real numbers.

2. Range:

Set of values, a dependent variable can take corresponding to the values of independent variables is called Range. For the function $A = f(a)$, the range of 'A' is also all positive real numbers.

For a function $h(x) = |x + 4|$, the domain of x is **real number**, and the range of $h(x)$ is **positive real number**.

Example 1: If $f(x) = 2x^3 - 3x^2 - 2x + 4$, find $f(2)$.

Plug in the value of $x = 2$ in the function,

we get $f(2) = 2.2^3 - 3.2^2 - 2.2 + 4 = 16 - 12 - 4 + 4 = 4$.

Example 2: If $g(t) = 2t^3 - 3t^2 - \frac{3}{t^2} + \frac{2}{t^3}$, find $g(\frac{1}{t})$.

$g(1/t) = 2(1/t)^3 - 3(1/t)^2 - \frac{3}{(1/t)^2} + \frac{2}{(1/t)^3} = \frac{2}{t^3} - \frac{3}{t^2} - 3t^2 + 2t^3$; this is in fact $g(t)$,

so $g(\frac{1}{t}) = g(t)$.

Compound functions:

When a function itself acts as an independent variable, it is called a compound function.
$f(g(x))$ is compound function.

Example 3: If $f(x) = 2x + 2$, and $g(x) = x^2$, then find $f(g(x))$ & $g(f(x))$.

$f(g(x)) = f(x^2) = 2.x^2 + 2 = 2(x^2 + 1)$; replace the value of x in $f(x) = 2x + 2$ with x^2.

and $g(f(x)) = g(2x + 2) = (2x + 2)^2 = 4x^2 + 8x + 4$; replace the value of x in $g(x) = x^2$ with $(2x + 2)$.

Example 4: If $f(x) = 3x - 2$, and $f(g(x)) = 2x$, then find $g(x)$.

$f(g(x)) = 2x$

$=> 3.g(x) - 2 = 2x$; replace the value of x in $f(x) = 3x - 2$ with $g(x)$.

$=> 3.g(x) = 2x + 2$

$=> g(x) = \dfrac{2(x + 1)}{3}$

The next section of the book gives you over 100+ practice equations. It does not have problems on GRE specify question types. The purpose of the book is to sharpen your math fundamentals. Once you sharpen your fundamentals on the GRE math, you will be in a better position to solve GRE QR questions.

Subsequent books on 'Word Problem', 'Algebra', 'Arithmetic', 'Geometry', 'Permutation and Combination', and 'Sets and Statistics' are solely dedicated on GRE question types.

–

Chapter 4

Practice Questions

4.1 Numbers and Digits

Q1. Identify rational and irrational numbers.

 (1) $\pi = 3.141592653589793238...$

 (2) $12.2367324902...$

 (3) $1.7373737373...$

 (4) $0.\overline{02}$

 (5) π^2

Q2. Write $6.\overline{52}$ in a rational fraction.

Q3. Write $0.\overline{524}$ in a rational fraction.

Q4. There are two positive integers a and b , and two negative integers c and d. Each ends with digit '2'. What would be unit digit of $(a + b + c + d)$?

Q5. If a decimal number $25.4n8$, rounded to the nearest tenth is less than 25.5, what is the set of values for n?

Q6. What is the value of $77,567,893 \times 10^{-6}$ rounded off to the nearest whole number?

4.2 Even/Odd and Consecutive Integers

Q1. If $a + b$ is even, is ab even? Given that a and b are positive integers.

Q2. If (pq) and r are even, is $(p + r)$ even?

Q3. If x, y, and z are consecutive integers, is xyz even?

Q4. If x is even, y, and z are odd, is $z(x + y)$ even?

Q5. What if the questions is: If z is even, is $z(x + y)$ even?

Q6. What if the questions is: If y, & z are odd, is $z(x + y)$ even?

Q7. What if the questions is: If y is even, & z is odd, is $z(x + y)$ even?

Q8. If n is an even integer, which of the following is an odd integer?

  A. $n^2 + 3$

  B. $3n^2 - 3$

  C. $n^3 + 2$

  D. $2n + 3$

  E. $-3n + 3$

  F. $n(n^4 - 3n^3 + 14n^2 - 4)$

  G. $\sqrt{n^2 + 12}$

Q9. If p, q, r, s and t are consecutive integers, is their sum even?

Q10. What if the questions is: If p, q, r, and s are consecutive integers, is their sum even?

4.3 Divisibility

Q1. The remainder is 37 when a number is divided by 10,000. What is the remainder when the same number is divided by 1,000?

Q2. If a is completely divisible by 7 and 18, is $\dfrac{a}{42}$ an integer?

Q3. If 70 is a factor of x, is 20 a factor of x?

Q4. If p is divisible by 15 and 14, is it divisible by 35?

Q5. If p is a factor of x, and x is a factor of y, is p a factor of y?

Q6. If x and y are multiples of 12, is $3x + 7y$ a multiple of 12?

Q7. If $\dfrac{x}{y}$ an odd integer, is x odd? Given that x and y are positive integers.

Q8. If 4611 is divisible by 159, is it also divisible by 53?

Q9. Two positive integers p and q when divided by 7 leave remainders of 3, and 4 respectively. Also given that $p > q$. What is the reminder if $p - q$ is divided by 7?

Q10. If 9 is a factor of both x and y, is $x + y$ divisible by 9?

Q11. If n is a positive integer and $(n + 1)(n + 3)$ is odd, then what is the minimum possible value of $(n + 2)(n + 4)$?

Q12. If above questions is altered as: If n is a **negative** integer and $(n + 1)(n + 3)$ is odd, then what is the minimum possible value of $(n + 2)(n + 4)$?

4.4   Simplification

Q1. Simplify $4 - [6 - 3^4(6 \div 3 + 1)]$.

Q2. $8 \div \left(\dfrac{8}{7} \times 25\% \text{ of } 28 \right)$.

Q3. Simplify $(9.75 \times 10^{-2}) - (25 \times 10^{-3})$.

Q4. What is the value of p, if $3\sqrt[3]{p} + 92 = -100$.

Q5. Simplify $(7.75 \times 10^2) \div (25 \times 10^{-3})$.

Q6. Simplify $\sqrt[9]{0.000000512}$.

Q7. If $m \neq 4$ and $m \neq 3$, then what is the value of $\dfrac{4m^2 - 64}{m - 4} - \dfrac{4m^2 - 36}{m - 3}$?

Q8. If $x = 0.999$, $y = \sqrt{0.999}$, and $z = (0.999)^2$, which among x, y and z is the largest and the smallest?

Q9. Between which two integers, the value of $\sqrt{30}$ lies?

Q10. Between which two integers the value of $\sqrt[3]{50}$ lies?

4.5   Exponents

Q1. Simplify $\dfrac{3^{t+3} + 3^t}{2 \times 3^t}$.

Q2. Simplify $64^{\frac{1}{3}} + 16^{\frac{1}{2}} + \dfrac{4}{(16)^0}$.

Q3. Simplify $\dfrac{(-4)^3 \times (2^5)^3}{-4^{-3}}$.

Q4. The expression $\left(\dfrac{-9}{4} \right)^{-2}$ is equivalent to the following EXCEPT.

A. $\left(\dfrac{-4}{9}\right)^{2}$

B. $\left(\dfrac{4}{9}\right)^{2}$

C. $\left(\dfrac{3}{2}\right)^{-4}$

D. $\left(\dfrac{2}{3}\right)^{4}$

E. $\left(\dfrac{2}{3}\right)^{-4}$

Q5. If $4^{x-1}.(0.5)^{3-2x} = \left(\dfrac{1}{8}\right)^{-x}$, what is the value of x?

Q6. If $3^{m+n} = \sqrt{p-4}$, and $m = 2 - n$, what is the value of p?

Q7. If n is an integer, and 0.00876×10^{n} is greater than 1000, what is the least possible value of n?

Q8. If a number $46567 \div 10^{-n}$ lies between 4 and 400, what is set of integer values of n?

Q9. If a number -0.046567×10^{n} lie between –3 and –500, what is set of integer values of n?

4.6   Factors/Multiples and LCM/HCF

Q1. If $11x$ is a multiple of 16500, is x a multiple of 70?

Q2. If 21 and 10 are factors of a number n, is 14 also a factor of n?

Q3. If x, y, and z are prime numbers such that $x < y < z$, and $xyx = 561$, what is the value of $z - y$?

Q4. X and Y are both two-digit numbers, with $X > Y$. If X and Y contain the same digits, but in reverse order, which of the following must be a factor of $(X - Y)$?

  A. 4

  B. 5

  C. 6

  D. 9

  E. 11

Q5. If $(x - y)(x + y) = 143$, and $(x - y)$ and $(x + y)$ are prime, what could be the probable values of x and y ?

Q6. If $3p + 11q = 43$; where p and q are positive integers, what is the value of pq?

Q7. If $x = 35n$, and $y = 55n$; whether n is prime, what is the greatest common factor of x and y?

4.7   Fraction

Q1. If x is $\dfrac{45}{47}$ of $\dfrac{47}{43}$, and y equals reciprocal of $\dfrac{45}{43}$, then what is the value of $\dfrac{x}{y}$?

Q2. Brian ate 1/3, and Suzy ate some fraction of the cookies, and then Rachel ate 1/2 of the remaining cookies. If 1/6 of the cookies are left in the jar, what fraction of the cookies was eaten by Suzy?

Q3. Which of the following fractions is larger?

A. $\dfrac{45}{44}, \dfrac{91}{92}$

B. $\dfrac{45}{44}, \dfrac{93}{92}$

C. $\dfrac{44}{45}, \dfrac{91}{92}$

D. $\dfrac{83}{81}, \dfrac{114}{111}$

4.8   Rationalization of factions

Q1. Rationalize $\dfrac{4}{3\sqrt{2}} - \dfrac{2}{\sqrt{2}}$.

Q2. Simplify $\dfrac{\sqrt{50}}{\sqrt{10}} \times \dfrac{\sqrt{18}}{\sqrt{12}}$.

4.9   Linear and Quadratic Equations

Q1. For the following two linear equations, find out the values of x and y.

$$x - 2y - 1 = 0 \ \&$$
$$-3y - x - 1 = 0$$

Q2. For the following two linear equations, find out the values of x and y.

$$\frac{x}{2} - \frac{y}{3} + 4 = 0 \ \&$$

$$x - \frac{y}{2} = -7$$

Q3. For $2x^2 + 7x + 3 = 0$, what are the values of x?

Q4. For $x - 3\sqrt{x} + 2 = 0$, what are the values of x?

Q5. For $x^{2/3} + x^{1/3} - 2 = 0$, what are the values of x?

Q6. For what values of m does the quadratic equation $x^2 + 2(m - 4)x + 2m = 0$ has equal roots.

Q7. If $(4x - 1)^2 = 81$, what is x?

Q8. If $(a - 3)(a + 2) = (a + 3)(a - 2)$, how many unique values a can have?

Q9. If $a^3 - a^2 - a + 1 = 0$, how many unique values a can have?

4.10   Absolute numbers

Q1. If $|10x| - 20 = 0$, what is x?

Q2. What is the value of $\left[\dfrac{-|-3| \times -|3|}{(-|-3|)^2} \right]$?

Q3. If $|2x - 5| = 8$, what is x?

4.11   Inequalities

Q1. How many values x might have for the inequality: $1 \le x < 3$?

Q2. If $\dfrac{1}{p} > 1$, what is the range of value of p?

Q3. What do following inequalities suggest about the values of a, and b?

  a. $ab > 0$

  b. $ab < 0$

  c. $ab = 0$

  d. $\dfrac{a}{b} > 0$

  e. $\dfrac{a}{b} < 0$

Q4. For which values of x, will the inequality $|2x - 1| < 5$ be true?

Q5. Solve the $|x + 2| < 7$ inequality for x.

Q6. Solve the inequality $|1 - 2x| < 9$ for x.

Q7. Solve the inequality $\dfrac{5x - 1}{-6} \leq \dfrac{1 - 2x}{3}$ for x.

Q8. If $1 < x < 3$, then which of the following could be true?

   I. $x^2 < 2x$

  II. $x^2 = 2x$

 III. $x^2 > 2x$

  A. I only

  B. II only

  C. III only

  D. I and II only

  E. All three

Q9. What does the inequality $ab^2c < 0$ suggest for the values of a, b and c?

Q10. If $8 > x > 3$ and $4 < y < 6$, what is the range of values of $(x - y)$?

Q11. If $6 < x < 12$ and $y = x + 4$, what is the greatest possible integer value of $(x + y)$?

Q12. For what values of x, the inequality: $x^2 > -6x - 5$?

Q13. For what values of x, the inequality: $x^2 > 6x - 5$?

4.12 Percents (practice)

Q1. 24 is 8% of what number? 300

Q2. If an industrial worker rejects 0.03% of screws as defective, how many screws does he examine to reject 300 screws? 1 million

Q3. What percent of 17 is 30 percent of 289? 510% of 17 = 86.7 which is 30% of 289.

Q4. How much you have to pay for an item priced $800, and discounted at 40%? 480

Q5. An item was sold at $100; it was bought for $120. What is the percent loss?

Q6. An item was bought at $100 after a discount of $20 on Marked Price. What is the percent discount on the Marked Price?

Q7. If X is more than Y by 110%, and Z is less than X by 10%, then X is what % of Z?

Q8. If a number is first increased by 20%, and then decreased by 20%, is the resulting number equal to the original number? no

Q9. A shopkeeper increased the price of his articles by 25%. What percent discount should he offer so that he does not run into losses? max 20%

4.13 Ratio & Proportion

Q1. If $0.25 : 5 :: x : 4$, then x=?

Q2. Two numbers are respectively 20% and 50% more than the third number. What is the ratio of the two numbers?

Q3. If $529 be divided into three parts, proportional to $\frac{1}{2} : \frac{2}{3} : \frac{3}{4}$, then what is the value of the third part?

Q4. A and B together have $240. If $\frac{3}{5}$ of A's amount is equal to $\frac{2}{5}$ of B's amount, how much does B have?

Q5. Two number are in the ratio of 3 : 5. If 9 is subtracted from each, new numbers are in the ratio of 12 : 23. What is the value of the larger number?

Q6. If $A : B : C = 2 : 3 : 4$, then find $\frac{A}{B} : \frac{B}{C} : \frac{C}{A}$.

Q7. A 60 liters mixture has milk and water in the ratio of 2 : 1. If the ratio is to be reversed, then what quantity of water should be added?

Q8. The sum of three numbers is 190. If the ratio of the first to second is 2 : 3 and that of the second to the third is also 2 : 3, then the third number is:

Q9. The salaries of A, B and C are of ratio of 2 : 3 : 5. If the increments of 15%, 10% and 20% are done to their respective salaries, then find the new ratio of their salaries.

Q10. If three numbers are in the ratio of 2 : 3 : 5, and the sum of their squares is 1368, what is the value of the first number?

4.14 Simple Interest

Q1. Find the simple interest on $8000 borrowed at $\frac{50}{3}$% for 27 months.

Q2. Brian took a loan for 6 years at the rate of 5% per annum on simple interest, If the total interest paid was $1230, what was the principal?

Q3. If a sum becomes four times of itself in 15 years, find simple rate of interest.

Q4. Brian borrows $5000 for 2 years at 4% p.a. simple interest. He immediately lends whole money to Suzy at $\frac{25}{4}$% p.a. for 2 years. Find the gain for Brian.

Q5. A lent $5000 to B for 2 years and $3000 to C for 4 years on simple interest at the same rate of interest and received $2200 in all from both of them as interest. What is the rate of interest per annum?

4.15 Compound Interest

Q1. Find the compound interest on $7500 at 4% per annum for 2 years, compounded annually.

Q2. Simple interest on a certain sum for 3 years at 8% per annum is equal to half the compound interest on $4000 for 2 years at 10% per annum. What is the sum placed on simple interest?

Q3. If the difference between simple interest and compound interest compounded annually on a certain sum of money for 2 years at 4% per annum is $1, find the sum.

Q4. What will be an effective annual rate of interest corresponding to nominal rate of 20% per annum, compounded half yearly?

Q5. If a sum of money invested at compound interest amounts to $800 in 3 years and to $840 in 4 years, what is the rate of interest per annum?

4.16 Functions

Q1. Given $f(x) = 2x - 7$, for what value of x, does $3f(x) - 3 = f(2x - 6)$?

Q2. For all positive integers p, $[p] = -|\sqrt{p}|$ when p is odd and $[p] = \frac{p}{5}$ when p is even. What is the value of [25]*[10]?

Q3. If $[m]$ is the greatest integer less than or equal to m, what is the value of $[-2.2] + [2.6] + [6.2]$?

Q4. An operation # is defined by the equation $a \# b = \dfrac{(a + b)}{(a^2 + b^2)}$, for all numbers a and b such that $a \neq 0$. If $a \# c = 0$, then what is the value of c in terms of a?

Q5. Given $f(x) = \dfrac{2x}{2x - 1}$, for what value of x, does $f(f(x)) = -1$?

Q6. Given $f(x) = \dfrac{2x}{2x - 1}$ and $g(x) = \dfrac{2x - 1}{2x}$, for what value of x, does $f(g(x)) = 3$?

Q7. If $f(x) = 2x + \sqrt{x}$, what is the value of $f(p^2 - 10p + 25)$?

Chapter 5

Answer Key

Numbers and Digits

1.1: Irrational;	1.2: Irrational;	1.3: Rational;	1.4: Rational;	1.5: Irrational
2: $\dfrac{646}{99}$	3: $\dfrac{524}{999}$	4: 0	5: $n = \{0, 1, 2, 3, 4, 5\}$	6: 78

Even/Odd and Consecutive Integers

1: Indeterminable	2: Indeterminable	3: Yes	4: No	5: Yes
6: Indeterminable	7: Indeterminable	8: A, B, D, & E	9: Indeterminable	10: Yes

Divisibility

1: 37	2: Yes	3: Indeterminable	4: Yes	5: Yes
6: Yes	7: Indeterminable	8: Yes	9: 6	10: Yes
11: 24	12: 0			

Simplification

1: 241	2: 1	3: 0.0725	4: -2^{18}	5: 31000
6: 0.2	7: 4	8: y: Largest z: Smallest	9: 5 & 6	10: 3 & 4

Exponents

1: 14	2: 12	3: 2^{27}	4: E	5: 5
6: 85	7: 6	8: $\{-3, -4\}$	9: $\{2, 3, 4\}$	

123

Factors/Multiples and LCM/HCF

1: Cannot say   2: Yes   3: 6   4: D   5: $\{12, \pm 1\}$

6: 14   7: $5n$

Fraction

1: $\left(\dfrac{45}{43}\right)^2$ 2: 1/3   3.A: $\dfrac{45}{44}$ 3.B: $\dfrac{45}{44}$ 3.C: $\dfrac{91}{92}$

3.D: $\dfrac{114}{111}$

Rationalization of fraction

1: $-\dfrac{\sqrt{2}}{3}$ 2: $\dfrac{\sqrt{30}}{2}$

Linear and Quadratic Equations

1: $x = \dfrac{1}{5}$, & $y = -\dfrac{2}{5}$ 2: $x = -4$, & $y = 6$ 3: -3 or $-\dfrac{1}{2}$ 4: 4 or 1   5: -8 or 1

6: 8 or 2   7: $\dfrac{5}{2}$ or -2 8: One   9: Two

Absolute numbers

1: $x = \pm 2$ 2: 1   3: $-\dfrac{3}{2}$ or $\dfrac{13}{2}$

Inequalities

1: Infinite   2: $0 < p < 1$ 3.a: $a > 0,\ \&\ b > 0$ 3.b: $a > 0,\ \&\ b < 0$ 3.c: $a\ =\ 0,\ \&/\text{or}$
                                            or   or $b = 0$
                                           $a < 0,\ \&\ b < 0$ $a < 0,\ \&\ b > 0$

3.d: $a > 0,\ \&\ b > 0$ 3.e: $a > 0,\ \&\ b < 0$ 4: $-2 < x < 3$ 5: $-9 < x < 5$ 6: $-4 < x < 5$
or   or
    $a < 0,\ \&\ b < 0$ $a < 0,\ \&\ b > 0$

7: $x \geq -1$ 8: E   9: a & c have   10: $4 > x - y > -3$ 11: 27

                                        opposite signs;
                                          sign of b cannot
                                          be determined

12: $x > -1$ or $x < -5$ 13: $x < 1$ or $x > 5$

Percents

1: 300   2: 1,000,000   3: 510   4: $480   5: 16.67%

6: 16.67%   7: 111.11%   8: No; less by 4%   9: 20%

Ratio & Proportion

1: 1/5   2: 4:5   3: 207   4: 144   5: 55

6: 8:9:24   7: 60 liters   8: 90   9: $23 : 33 : 60$ 10: 12

Simple Interest

1: $3000   2: $4100   3: 20%   4: $225   5: 10%

Compound Interest

1: $612   2: $1750   3: $625   4: 21% p.a.   5: 5%

Functions

1: $x = 5/2$ 2: -10 3: 5   4: $-a$ 5: $-1/6$

6: 2   7: $2p^2 - 19p + 45$;
            $2p^2 - 21p + 55$.

Chapter 6

Solutions

6.1 Numbers and Digits

Q1.

(1) Irrational; π is an irrational number as the decimal does not terminate and has no repeated pattern.

(2) Irrational; decimal does not terminate and has no repeated pattern.

(3) Rational; decimal has a repeated pattern.

(4) Rational; decimal has a repeated pattern.

(5) Irrational; exponent of an irrational number would be an irrational number.

Q2.

· Step 1: Say $x = 6.\overline{52}$.

· Step 2: Now multiply x with a minimum value of exponent of 10 such that recurring part of the number x becomes an integer. So, $100x = 652.\overline{52}$.

· Step 3: Now deduct $x = 6.\overline{52}$ from $100x = 652.\overline{52}$; we get $99x = 646$ or $x = \dfrac{646}{99}$; a rational fraction.

Q3.

· Step 1: Say $x = 0.\overline{524}$.

· Step 2: Now multiply x with a minimum value of exponent of 10 such that recurring part of the number x becomes an integer. So, $1000x = 524.\overline{524}$.

· Step 3: Now deduct $x = 0.\overline{524}$ from $1000x = 524.\overline{524}$; we get $999x = 524$ or $x = \dfrac{524}{999}$; a rational fraction.

Q4. 0.

The numbers a, b, c, and d can have any number of digits; however for this question, it is not of any importance to know how many digits each number has as while adding numbers, we add unit digits first; so the addition of unit digits of a, b, c, and d would be $2 + 2 + (-2) + (-2) = 4 - 4 = 0$.

Alternatively, you can assume some values for a, b, c, and d. Say $a = 2452, b = 32, c = -82$, and $d = -2$. It is clear that the unit digit of the sum of a, b, c, and d would be 0.

Q5.

It is to be noted that n must be less than '5' as if it were '5' or more than '5', the tenth digit '4' would be rounded off to '5' and the number would be '25.5'. Remember that if the digit to the left of '5' is even (In this case it is '4'), it is not increased by '1'. So, to keep the number less than '25.5', the set of $n = \{0, 1, 2, 3, 4\}$.

Q6.

$77,567,893 \times 10^{-6} = 77.567893$. Since we have to round off to the nearest whole number, the number 77.567893 would be '78' as the digit on its tenth place is '5' which means that we must increase the digit to its left by '1' or the digit on tens place '7' becomes '8'. We need not dig more to deduce what digit would the tenth place digit '5' would be when rounded off from the extreme right of the number, starting with the right-most digit '3', as even if the tenth place digit were '6', the treatment to the tens place digit '7' would not change.

6.2 Even/Odd and Consecutive Integers

Q1.

Sum of two integers can be even in two situations:

(1) Both a and b are even. For example, $a = 2$, and $b = 4$. Sum $= 2 + 4 = 6$ (Even). This gives $ab = 8$; an even number.

(2) Both a and b are odd. For example, $a = 1$, and $b = 3$. Sum $= 1 + 3 = 4$ (Even). This gives $ab = 3$; an odd number. So it is indeterminable whether ab is odd or even.

Q2.

So, the situation is: Is (p+even) even? It will depend on the nature of p; if it is even, (p+even) would be even, else odd.

Given is pq = even, but this will not help us anyway as for pq to be even p can be even and q can be odd, or vice-versa. So the nature of $(p + r)$ is indeterminable.

Q3.

Consecutive integers may start from an even integer, say {2, 3, 4}, or an odd integer, say {3, 4, 5}. In either case, at least one of the consecutive integers, x, y, and z is even. And we know that the product of an even integer either with an even or an odd integer is an even integer; therefore, the product xyz must be even.

Q4. No.

So the situation is $z(x + y)$ = Odd.(Even + Odd) = Odd.Odd = Odd. The answer is No. $z(x + y)$ is odd.

Q5. Yes.

$z(x + y)$ is even. The situation is $z(x + y)$ = Even.$(x + y)$ = Even.(Odd) or Even.(Even); however both are even; it is insignificant to know what the nature of $(x + y)$ is.

Q6. Indeterminable.

The situation is $z(x + y)$ = Odd.$(x+$Odd$)$. Since Odd.Even = Even and Odd.Odd = Odd, it is necessary to know the nature of $(x+$Odd$)$; if x is even, $(x+$Odd$)$ is odd, and if x is odd, $(x+$Odd$)$ is even. So it is indeterminable.

Q7. Indeterminable.

Follow the same reasoning as used in the above questions.

Q8.

Let us abbreviate Even as 'E' and Odd as 'O'.

We know that Even $\times$ Even = Even & Even $\times$ Odd = Even, and Even + Even = Even & Even + Odd = Odd.

   A. $n^2 + 3$: The expression is equivalent to $E^2 + O = E.E + O = E + O = O$; it is an **odd number**.

B. $3n^2 - 3$: The expression is equivalent to $O.E^2 - O = O.E - O = E - O = O$; it is an **odd number**.

C. $n^3 + 2$: The expression is equivalent to $E^3 + E = E + E = E$; it is an even number.

D. $2n + 3$: The expression is equivalent to $E.E + O = E + O = O$; it is an **odd number**.

E. $-3n + 3$: The expression is equivalent to $-O.E + O = -E + O = O$; it is an **odd number**.

F. $n(n^4 - 3n^3 + 14n^2 - 4)$: The expression is equivalent to $E.(\text{Unknown number: Even or Odd}) = E.(O \text{ or } E) = E$; multiplication of any number with an even number is always even.

G. $\sqrt{n^2 + 12}$: The expression is equivalent to $\sqrt{E^2 + E} = \sqrt{E + E} = \sqrt{E}$; square root of an even number may be even or real, but cannot be an odd number.

The correct answers are option A, B, D, & E.

Q9.

There would be two situations:

(1) The five consecutive integers starting with an even integer are {2, 5, 6, 7, 8}; the sum is even.

(2) The five consecutive integers starting with an odd integer are {1, 2, 5, 6, 7}; the sum is odd. So it is indeterminable.

Q10.

Again there would be two situations:

(1) The four consecutive integers starting with an even integer are {2, 5, 6, 7}; the sum is even.

(2) The four consecutive integers starting with an odd integer are {1, 2, 5, 6}; the sum is even. So the sum is even.

Remember that sum of even number of consecutive integers is always even.

6.3 Divisibility

Q1.

Say the number is $(10000n+37)$; where n is a positive integer. Since $10000n$ is divisible by 1000, the question comes down to whether 37 is divisible by 1000. Since it is not divisible by 1000, the remainder would be 37 only.

Q2.

Since a is completely divisible by 7, a would be $7n$, where n is a positive integer; similarly, since a is completely divisible by 18, a would be $18m$; where m is a positive integer. But a can be any one value between $7n$ or $18m$. Since 7 and 18 are co-prime to each other, a should be $7 \times 18p$; where p is a positive integer.

Two numbers are co-prime to each other if a factor other than '1' is common between them.

Now, is $\frac{a}{42}$ an integer? We plug in the value of a, and get $\frac{a}{42} = \frac{7 \times 18p}{2.3.7} = \frac{7 \times 2 \times 3 \times 3p}{2.3.7} = 3p$ (an integer); so $\frac{a}{42}$ is an integer.

Q3.

For 20 to be a factor of x given that 70 is a factor of x, 20 must be a factor of 70—which is not true. So whether 20 is a factor of x is indeterminable. Note that 20 may or may not be a factor of x. Let us see how it may be a factor of x.

Say $x = 70n$; where n is a positive integer. For 20 to be a factor of x, $\frac{70n}{20}$ must be an integer. After reducing $\frac{70n}{20}$, we get $\frac{7n}{2}$. If n is a multiple of 2, 20 is a factor of x, else not.

Another approach would be: say if $x = 140$ (a multiple of 70), then 20 is a factor of x; however if $x = 210$ (a multiple of 70), then 20 is NOT a factor of x. So it is inconclusive!

Q4.

The answer is Yes. Since prime factors of $35 = \{5, 7\}$ are common either with the prime factors of $15=\{3, 5\}$ or with the prime factors of $14 = \{2, 7\}$, p is divisible by 35.

Another approach would be: Since p is a multiple of 15 and 14, p must be a multiple of all the factors of 15 and 14. This means that $p = 3.5.7.n = 35.(3n)$; where n is a positive integer. It is clear that p is a multiple of 35 or is divisible by 35.

Q5.

Say $x = pn$ and $y = xm$; where n & m are positive integers. So $y = pnm$, and we can deduce that p a factor of y.

Q6.

Say $3x + 7y = 3(12n) + 7(12m) = 12(3n + 7m)$; where n & m are positive integers. It is clear that $12(3n + 7m)$ is a multiple of 12.

Q7.

$\dfrac{x}{y}$ can be odd in two situations:

(1) Both x and y are even, and x is a multiple of an odd number. For example, $x = 12$, and $y = 4$, so $\dfrac{x}{y} = \dfrac{12}{4} = 3$; an odd number.

(2) Both x and y are odd. For example, $x = 21$, and $y = 7$, so $\dfrac{x}{y} = \dfrac{21}{7} = 3$ (an odd number). So it is indeterminable whether x is odd or even.

Q8. Yes.

Since 53 is factor of a 159, $(159 = 53.3)$, 4611 will also be divisible by 53. Remember that if a divisor x divides a number y completely, all the factors of x will also divide y completely.

Q9.

Say $p = 7n + 3$ and $q = 7m + 4$, so $p - q = 7(n - m) - 1$; where n and m are positive integers. The term $7(n - m)$ is divisible by 7 as it is a multiple of 7, so the remainder is -1.

What is the significance of remainder: 1?

Well, the remainder cannot be negative, it means that the remainder is $7 - 1 = 6$.

If the Derived Remainder is negative, **Actual Remainder = Divisor — | Derived Remainder |**.

Alternatively, you can assume some values for p and q. Say $p = 7 + 3 = 10$ and $q = 7 + 4 = 11$, but these value are not feasible as we know that $p > q$. So, let

$p = 7.2 + 3 = 17$ and $q = 7 + 4 = 11$. Now $p - q = 17 - 11 = 6$. So, the remainder is $7 - 1 = 6$.

Q10.

Since 9 is a factor of x, as well as y, $x = 9n$ and $y = 9m$. So $x + y = 9n + 9m = 9(n + m)$, which is completely divisible by 9 or $(x + y)$ is divisible by 9.

Q11.

Since $(n + 1)(n + 3)$ is odd, and we know that if the product of two numbers is odd, both the numbers must be odd, $(n + 1)$ must be odd. Again, n is a positive integer and we are interested in its minimum value; hence the minimum positive integer n can have for $(n + 1)$ to be odd would be 2.

So the minimum possible value of $(n + 2)(n + 4) = (2 + 2)(2 + 4) = 4 \times 6 = 24$.

Q12.

Having discussed the previous questions, we already know that both the numbers $(n + 1)$ & $(n + 3)$ are odd. But n is a negative integer now; assuring that $(n + 1)$ & $(n + 3)$ remain odd, say we put $n = -2$, then $(n + 2)(n + 4) = (-2 + 2)(-2 + 4) = 0.2 = 0$.

If we try with smaller negative numbers for n, on the contrary, the result would not be minimum, it would rather be larger. Say we put $n = -6$, then then $(n + 2)(n + 4) = (-6 + 2)(-6 + 4) = -4. - 2 = 8$.

So the minimum possible value of $(n + 2)(n + 4) = 0$. Remember that $n = -2$ is the not the only negative value to make $(n + 2)(n + 4)$ minimum, it can also be minimum at $n = -4$.

6.4 Simplification

Q1.

$4 - [6 - 3^4(6 \div 3 + 1)]$

$\Rightarrow 4 - [6 - 3^4(\frac{6}{3} + 1)]$; innermost parenthesis first, and 'division' before 'addition'

$\Rightarrow 4 - [6 - 3^4(2 + 1)]$; performing division

$\Rightarrow 4 - [6 - 3^4(3)]$; performing addition

=> $4 - [6 - 81.(3)]$; expanding exponent

=> $4 - [6 - 243]$; performing multiplication

=> $4 - [-237]$; performing subtraction

=> $4 + 237$; performing multiplication of two negatives

=> 241; performing addition

Q2.

$8 \div \left(\dfrac{8}{7} \times 25\% \text{ of } 28 \right)$

=> $8 \div \left(\dfrac{8}{7} \times \dfrac{25}{100} \times 28 \right)$

=> $8 \div \left(\dfrac{8}{7} \times \dfrac{\cancel{25}}{\cancel{100}_{4}} \times \cancel{28}^{7} \right)$

=> $8 \div \left(\dfrac{8}{\cancel{7}} \times \cancel{7} \right)$

=> $8 \div 8$

=> $1.$

Q3.

$(9.75 \times 10^{-2}) - (25 \times 10^{-3})$

=> $0.0975 - 0.025$

=> 0.0725

Alternatively, we can simplify in the following way.

$(9.75 \times 10^{-2}) - (25 \times 10^{-3})$

=> $(9.75 \times 10^{-2}) - (\dfrac{25}{10} \times 10^{-2})$

=> $10^{-2}[9.75 - 2.5]$

=> $10^{-2}[7.25]$

=> $\dfrac{7.25}{100}$

=> 0.0725

Q4.

$3\sqrt[3]{p} + 92 = -100$

=> $3\sqrt[3]{p} = -192$

=> $\sqrt[3]{p} = -\dfrac{192}{3}$

=> $\sqrt[3]{p} = -64$

=> $p = (-64)^3 = -2^{18}$.

Q5.

$(7.75 \times 10^2) \div (25 \times 10^{-3})$

=> $\dfrac{7.75 \times 10^2}{25 \times 10^{-3}}$

=> $\dfrac{775}{25 \times 10^{-3}}$

=> $\dfrac{\cancel{775}^{\,31} \times 10^3}{\cancel{25}}$

=> 31000.

Q6.

$\sqrt[9]{0.000000512}$

=> $(0.000000512)^{1/9}$

=> $(512 \times 10^{-9})^{1/9}$

=> $(512)^{1/9} \times 10^{(-9 \times 1/9)}$

=> $2^{(9 \times 1/9)} \times 10^{-1}$

=> 2×10^{-1}

=> 0.2.

Q7.

$\dfrac{4m^2 - 64}{m - 4} - \dfrac{4m^2 - 36}{m - 3}$ can be simplified as

$= \dfrac{4(m^2 - 16)}{m - 4} - \dfrac{4(m^2 - 9)}{m - 3}$

$= \dfrac{4(m + 4)\,(\cancel{m - 4})}{(\cancel{m - 4})} - \dfrac{4(m + 3)\,(\cancel{m - 3})}{(\cancel{m - 3})}$

$= 4m + 16 - 4m - 12$

$= 4.$

Q8.

Note that the base number $0.999 < 1$. Remember that...

(1) n^{th} root of a number less than 1 is always greater than the number itself; so $0.999 < \sqrt{0.999}$.

(2) Squares, cubes, and other high value powers of a number less than 1 are always smaller than the number itself; so $0.999 > (0.999)^2$.

It means that $z < x < y$. So, y is the largest, and z the smallest.

Apposite is true for a number greater than 1!

Q9.

First, find out which two perfect square numbers are closest to '30'; these are 25 and 36. So we can say that $(25 = 5^2) < 30 < (36 = 6^2)$ or $5 < \sqrt{30} < 6$. So $\sqrt{30}$ lies between 5 and 6.

Q10.

First, find out which two perfect cube numbers are closest to '50'; these are 27 and 64. So we can say that $(27 = 3^3) < 50 < (64 = 4^3)$ or $3 < \sqrt[3]{50} < 4$. So $\sqrt[3]{50}$ lies between 3 and 4.

6.5 Exponents

Q1.

$$\frac{3^{t+3} + 3^t}{2 \times 3^t}$$

$$= \frac{3^t.3^3 + 3^t}{2 \times 3^t}$$

$$= \frac{3^t.(3^3 + 1)}{2 \times 3^t}; \text{ taking } 3^t \text{ as common.}$$

$$= \frac{\cancel{3^t}.(27 + 1)}{2 \times \cancel{3^t}}$$

$$= 14.$$

Q2.

$$64^{\frac{1}{3}} + 16^{\frac{1}{2}} + \frac{4}{16^0}$$

$$= (2^6)^{\frac{1}{3}} + (2^4)^{\frac{1}{2}} + \frac{4}{1}; \text{ since } a^0 = 1$$

$$= 2^{6 \times 1/3} + 2^{4 \times 1/2} + 4$$

$$= 2^2 + 2^2 + 4$$

$$= 4 + 4 + 4 = 12.$$

Q3.

$$\frac{(-4)^3 \times (2^5)^3}{-4^{-3}}$$

$$= \frac{(-1)^3.4^3.2^{5 \times 3}}{-\dfrac{1}{4^3}}$$

$$= \frac{\cancel{-1}.4^3.4^3.2^{15}}{\cancel{-1}}; \text{ since } (-1)^{\text{odd}} = -1, \text{ and } (-1)^{\text{even}} = +1$$

$$= 4^6.2^{15}$$

$$= (2^2)^6.2^{15}$$

$$= 2^{2 \times 6}.2^{15}$$

$$= 2^{12}.2^{15}$$

$$= 2^{12+15}$$

$= 2^{27}$

Q4.

Let us solve the expression and get the desired equivalents.

$= \left(\dfrac{-9}{4}\right)^{-2} = \left(\dfrac{-4}{9}\right)^{2}$; when the exponent changes sign, numerator and denominator swap.

Option A is an equivalent expression.

$= \left(\dfrac{-4}{9}\right)^{2} = \left(\dfrac{4}{9}\right)^{2}$; 'negative number' raised to an even exponent is always positive.

Option B is an equivalent expression.

$\Rightarrow \left(\dfrac{-9}{4}\right)^{-2} = \left(\dfrac{9}{4}\right)^{-2} = \left(\dfrac{3^2}{2^2}\right)^{-2} = \left(\dfrac{3}{2}\right)^{-2\times2} = \left(\dfrac{3}{2}\right)^{-4}$.

Option C is an equivalent expression.

$\Rightarrow$ Similarly, $\left(\dfrac{3}{2}\right)^{-4} = \left(\dfrac{2}{3}\right)^{4}$; when the exponent changes sign, numerator and denominator swap.

Option D is an equivalent expression.

So the correct answer is option E.

Q5.

$4^{x-1}.(0.5)^{3-2x} = \left(\dfrac{1}{8}\right)^{-x}$

$\Rightarrow (2^2)^{x-1}.\left(\dfrac{5}{10}\right)^{3-2x} = \left(\dfrac{1}{2^3}\right)^{-x}$

$\Rightarrow 2^{2x-2}.\left(\dfrac{\cancel{5}}{\cancel{10}^{\,2}}\right)^{3-2x} = (2^{-3})^{-x}$

$\Rightarrow 2^{2x-2}.\left(\dfrac{1}{2}\right)^{3-2x} = 2^{-3\times-x}$

$\Rightarrow 2^{2x-2}.2^{-3+2x} = 2^{3x}$

$\Rightarrow 2^{2x-2-3+2x} = 2^{3x}$

=> $2^{4x-5} = 2^{3x}$

It means that $4x - 5 = 3x => \boldsymbol{x = 5}$; if bases are equal, exponents would be equal.

Q6.

Plug in the value of m in $3^{m+n} = \sqrt{p - 4}$, we get,

$3^{2-n+n} = \sqrt{p - 4}$; $m = 2 - n$

=> $3^2 = \sqrt{p - 4}$

=> $9 = \sqrt{p - 4}$

=> $9^2 = (\sqrt{p - 4})^2$; squaring both the sides.

=> $81 = p - 4$

=> $p = 85$.

Q7.

For the number 0.00876 to be greater than 1000, decimal must be moved six places to the right and the resulting number would be 8760 > 1000. This means that the number must be multiplied with 10^6. Hence the least possible value of $n = 6$.

Q8.

Only numbers 4.6567 and 46.567 would lie between 4 and 400. The number $46567 \div 10^{-n}$ can be written as 46567.0×10^n. To get the number 4.6567, we must move the decimal four places to its left in 46567.0, which means that the number must be multiplied with 10^{-4} or $n = -4$.

Similarly, to get the number 46.567, we must move the decimal three places to its left in 46567.0, which means that the number must be multiplied with 10^{-3} or $n = -3$. Hence the set of $n = \{-3, -4\}$.

Q9.

Numbers -4.6567, -46.567, and -465.67 would lie between -3 and -500. Which means that we must move the decimal two, three, and four places respectively to its right to get these numbers. Hence the set of $n = \{2, 3, 4\}$.

6.6   Factors/Multiples and LCM/HCF

Q1.

We cannot conclude. We can deduce that $11x = 16500n$; where n is a positive integer. So $\cancel{11}x = \cancel{16500}^{\,1500}n => x = 1500n$. It is clear that 1500 does not have any factor '7'. The answer is indeterminable or could be true because if $n = 7$, the answer is yes, else not!

Had the question been: If $11x$ is a multiple of 16500, MUST x be a multiple of 70? The would have been definite NO!.

Q2.

Since both the prime factors of 14 (2, 7) are common with either the prime factors of 21 (3, 7) or the prime factors of 10 (2, 5), 14 is also a factor of n.

Alternatively, since 21 (3, 7), and 10 (2, 7) are factors of n, so $n = 2.3.7.m = 210m$; where m is a positive integer. It is clear that '14' is factor of '210', or 14 also a factor of n.

Q3.

$xyz = 561$ can be factorized as a product of three prime numbers (3, 11, & 17) as $xyz = 561 = 3.11.17$; as per the condition x, y, and z must be different from each other & $x < y < z$, so only possible values of x, y, and z would be 3, 11, and 17 respectively. So $z - y = 17 - 11 = 6$.

Q4.

A two-digit number can be written as $10x + y$; where x is tens digit and y is unit digit. So $X = 10x + y$ and $Y = 10y + x$, as the digits are reversed.

$=> X - Y = (10x + y) - (10y + x) = 9x - 9y = 9(x - y)$; it is clear that 9 is factor of $(X - Y)$. So the correct option is D.

Q5.

Only prime factors of 143 are {11, 13}. Since the number 143 is a product of two primes, hence $(x - y)$ would be either 11 or 13, and vice-versa for $(x + y)$.

    (I) Say $x - y = 11$, and $x + y = 13$, so we get $x = 12$ and $y = 1$. So, one pair is {12, 1}.

(II) Say $x - y = 13$, and $x + y = 11$, so we get $x = 12$ and $y = -1$. So, one pair is $\{12, -1\}$.

It is to be noted that 143 cannot be equated to -11×-13 or -13×-11, because the prime numbers cannot be negative.

So there are total two set of possible pairs : $\{12, 1\}$, and $\{12, -1\}$.

Q6.

Looking at the linear equation: $3p + 11q = 43$, we may presume that the values of p and q are indeterminable as there are two unknown variables and only one equation is given, however it is not so. We have the second condition given in the question: 'p and q are positive integers'. Let's make use of it.

The equation $3p + 11q = 43$ can be written as $p = \dfrac{43 - 11q}{3}$. Since p is a positive integer, hence $(43 - 11q)$ must be divisible by 3. Let us plug in some positive integers for q, and see for what value of q, $(43 - 11q)$ is a multiple of 3.

For $q = 1, p = \dfrac{43 - 11.1}{3} = 32/3$ (not an integer); So we discard a probable value of q as 1.

For $q = 2, p = \dfrac{43 - 11.2}{3} = 21/3 = 7$ (an integer); So we take the value of q as 2; and p would be 7 and $pq = 7.2 = 14$.

There is no need to check further as the value of pq would be a finite number; however for your curiosity, we find that for $q = 3, p = \dfrac{43 - 11.3}{3} = 10/3$ is not an integer. There is no need to check even further as for $q = 4, p = \dfrac{43 - 11.4}{3} = -1/3$; negative numbers result, we are given that p is a positive integer, so we need not deep dive further.

So, we get $pq = 7.2 = 14$.

Q7.

Greatest common factor among numbers is also called HCF or GCD. The question asks us to find out the HCF of $35n$ and $55n$. Since $35n = 5.7.n$ and $55n = 5.11.n$ have '5' and 'n' as common, the HCF would be $5n$ or the greatest common factor of x and y is '$5n$'.

Alternatively,

$x = 5.7.n$;
$y = 5.11.n$;
––––––––-
HCF $= 5.n$
––––––––-

The answer is $5n$.

6.7 Fraction

Q1.

$x = \dfrac{45}{47} \times \dfrac{47}{43} = \dfrac{45}{43}$ &

$y =$ reciprocal of $\dfrac{45}{43} = \dfrac{43}{45}$

So, $\dfrac{x}{y} = \dfrac{\left(\dfrac{45}{43}\right)}{\left(\dfrac{43}{45}\right)} = \dfrac{45}{43} \times \dfrac{45}{43} = \dfrac{45^2}{43^2} = \left(\dfrac{45}{43}\right)^2$

$\Rightarrow \dfrac{x}{y} = \left(\dfrac{45}{43}\right)^2$

Q2.

Say Suzy ate $\left(\dfrac{1}{n}\right)^{\text{th}}$ fraction of cookies, then the fraction of cookies left after eaten up by Brian and Suzy $= 1 - \dfrac{1}{3} - \dfrac{1}{n} = \dfrac{2n-3}{3n}$.

Since 1/2 of $\dfrac{2n-3}{3n}$ was eaten by Rachel, $\dfrac{1}{2} \cdot \left(\dfrac{2n-3}{3n}\right) =$ Fraction of cookies left in the jar $= \dfrac{1}{6}$.

Or, $\dfrac{1}{2} \cdot \left(\dfrac{2n-3}{3n}\right) = \dfrac{2n-3}{6n}$

$\Rightarrow \dfrac{2n-3}{6n} = \dfrac{1}{6}$

$\Rightarrow n = 3$. Suzy ate $1/n = 1/3$ fraction of cookies.

Let us cross check...

Fraction of cookies left after eaten up by Brian and Suzy $= 1 - \dfrac{1}{3} - \dfrac{1}{3} = \dfrac{1}{3}$.

It means that Rachel ate $\frac{1}{2}$ of $\frac{1}{3}$ = $\frac{1}{6}$ fraction of cookies.

Fraction of cookies left in the jar = $1 - \frac{1}{3} - \frac{1}{3} - \frac{1}{6} = \frac{1}{6}$, which is equal to the fraction given in the equation. So our calculation was correct.

Alternatively...

Say total number of cookies were 6. We chose a smart number '6' as from the question, we know that we have to deal with the fractions: 1/3 and 1/2, so the LCM is 6, a convenient number.

Total cookies = 6;

Total cookies eaten by Brian = 1/3 of 6 = 2;

Say total cookies eaten by Suzy = x;

So, remaining cookies after eaten by Brian and Suzy = $6 - 2 - x = 4 - x$;

So, total cookies eaten by Rachel = 1/2 of $4 - x = \frac{4 - x}{2}$;

We know that the total cookies left in the jar = 1/6 of 6 = 1;

So, $x + \frac{4 - x}{2} = 2 + 1 = 3 \Rightarrow x = 2$; or Suzy ate $x/6 = 2/6 = 1/3$ fraction of cookies.

Q3.

A. $\frac{45}{44}, \frac{91}{92}$

The numerator of fraction $\frac{45}{44}$ is larger than its denominator, hence $\frac{45}{44} > 1$; whereas the numerator of fraction $\frac{91}{92}$ is smaller than its denominator, hence $\frac{91}{92} < 1$. So, $\frac{45}{44} > \frac{91}{92}$.

B. $\frac{45}{44}, \frac{93}{92}$

$\frac{45}{44}$ can be written as $\frac{45 + 1}{44} = 1\frac{1}{44}$; similarly $\frac{93}{92} = 1\frac{1}{92}$. The integer part of both the mixed fractions are equal (1) and the fraction part of $1\left|\frac{1}{44}\right|$ is greater than the fraction part of $1\left|\frac{1}{92}\right|$; $\left(\frac{1}{44} > \frac{1}{92}\right)$; smaller the denominator, larger is the fraction. So $\frac{45}{44} > \frac{93}{92}$.

C. $\dfrac{44}{45}, \dfrac{91}{92}$

$\dfrac{44}{45}$ can be written as $\dfrac{44-1}{44} = 1 - \dfrac{1}{44}$; similarly $\dfrac{91}{92} = 1 - \dfrac{1}{92}$. The integer part of both the mixed fractions are equal (1) and though the absolute vale of the fraction part of $1\left|-\dfrac{1}{44}\right|$ is greater than the fraction part of $1\left|-\dfrac{1}{92}\right|$, it is smaller since it is negative. $\left(-\dfrac{1}{44} < -\dfrac{1}{92}\right)$; So $\dfrac{44}{45} < \dfrac{91}{92}$.

D. $\dfrac{83}{81}, \dfrac{114}{111}$

$\dfrac{83}{81}$ can be written as $\dfrac{81+2}{81} = 1\dfrac{2}{81}$; similarly $\dfrac{114}{111} = 1\dfrac{3}{11}$. The integer part of both the mixed fractions are equal (1), but fraction parts cannot be compared as neither the numerator nor the denominator of the first fraction is equal to the relevant counterparts of the second fraction.

So the question reduces to: Which of two fractions is larger: $\dfrac{2}{81}$ or $\dfrac{3}{111}$?

The fraction $\dfrac{2}{81}$ can be written as $\dfrac{1}{81/2} = \dfrac{1}{\# > 40}$; similarly, the fraction $\dfrac{3}{111}$ can be written as $\dfrac{1}{111/3} = \dfrac{1}{\# < 40}$. Between the two factions $\dfrac{1}{\# > 40}$, and $\dfrac{1}{\# < 40}$, $\dfrac{1}{\# < 40}$ is larger because its denominator ($\# < 40$) is smaller than the denominator ($\# > 40$) of $\dfrac{1}{\# > 40}$.

So $\dfrac{2}{81} < \dfrac{3}{111}$ or $\dfrac{83}{81} < \dfrac{114}{111}$.

6.8 Rationalization of factions

Q1.

Rationalizing denominators of the fractions by multiplying the fractions by $\dfrac{\sqrt{2}}{\sqrt{2}}$, we get

$$\dfrac{\sqrt{2}}{\sqrt{2}} \times \left(\dfrac{4}{3\sqrt{2}} - \dfrac{2}{\sqrt{2}}\right) = \dfrac{4.\sqrt{2}}{3.\sqrt{2}.\sqrt{2}} - \dfrac{2.\sqrt{2}}{\sqrt{2}.\sqrt{2}} = \dfrac{4\sqrt{2}}{3.2} - \dfrac{2\sqrt{2}}{2} = \dfrac{4\sqrt{2}}{6} - \dfrac{2\sqrt{2}}{2} = \dfrac{\overset{2}{\cancel{4}}\sqrt{2}}{\underset{3}{\cancel{6}}} - \dfrac{\cancel{2}\sqrt{2}}{\cancel{2}} =$$

$$\dfrac{2\sqrt{2}}{3} - \sqrt{2} = \dfrac{2\sqrt{2} - 3\sqrt{2}}{3} = \dfrac{-\sqrt{2}}{3}.$$

$$\Rightarrow -\dfrac{\sqrt{2}}{3}.$$

Q2.

$\dfrac{\sqrt{50}}{\sqrt{10}} \times \dfrac{\sqrt{18}}{\sqrt{12}} = \dfrac{\sqrt{5^2.2}}{\sqrt{5.2}} \times \dfrac{\sqrt{3^2.2}}{\sqrt{2^2.3}} = \dfrac{5\sqrt{2}}{\sqrt{5}\sqrt{2}} \times \dfrac{3\sqrt{2}}{2\sqrt{3}} = \dfrac{15\sqrt{2}}{2\sqrt{3}\sqrt{5}}$; to rationalise the denominator, we multiply the faction with $\dfrac{\sqrt{3}.\sqrt{5}}{\sqrt{3}.\sqrt{5}}$.

$=> \left(\dfrac{\sqrt{3}\sqrt{5}}{\sqrt{3}\sqrt{5}} \right) \times \left(\dfrac{15\sqrt{2}}{2\sqrt{3}\sqrt{5}} \right) = \dfrac{15\sqrt{2}\sqrt{15}}{2.15} = \dfrac{\sqrt{30}}{2}$.

6.9 Linear and Quadratic Equations

Q1.

$$x - 2y - 1 = 0 ------(1) \ \&$$
$$-3y - x - 1 = 0 ------(2)$$

By multiplying eqn (2) with '-1', we get $3y + x + 1 = 0$.

Let us calculate the value of x in terms of y from the first equation and substitute it in the second equation.

$x - 2y - 1 = 0$
$=> x = 1 + 2y$

By plugging in x in eqn. (2), we get,

$3y + (1 + 2y) + 1 = 0$

$3y + 1 + 2y + 1 = 0$

$=> 5y = -2$

$=> y = -\dfrac{2}{5}$.

By plugging in the value of $y = -\dfrac{2}{5}$ in the equation $x = 1 + 2y$, we get $x = 1 + 2 \times -\dfrac{2}{5} = \dfrac{1}{5}$

So, $x = \dfrac{1}{5}$, and $y = -\dfrac{2}{5}$.

Q2.

$$\frac{x}{2} - \frac{y}{3} + 4 = 0 \text{ ---(1)}$$

$$x - \frac{y}{2} = -7 \text{ ---(2)}$$

There could be couple of approaches to solve these types of linear equations; we suggest that it is better to get rid of the denominator-constants from both the equations. The calls for taking LCM.

Taking LCM of the first eqn., and simplifying, we get,

$$\frac{x}{2} - \frac{y}{3} + 4 = 0 \Rightarrow 3x - 2y + 24 = 0 \text{ ---(3)}$$

Taking LCM of the second eqn., and simplifying, we get,

$$x - \frac{y}{2} = -7 \Rightarrow 2x - y = -14 \text{ ---(4)}$$

Now, we can calculate the value of y in terms of x from eqn. 4, so we get,

$$2x - y = -14 \text{ ---(4)}$$

$$y = 2x + 14 \text{ ---(4)}$$

By substituting the value of y in the first eqn, we get,

$$3x - 2y + 24 = 0 \text{ ---(1)}$$

$$\Rightarrow 3x - 2(2x + 14) + 24 = 0$$

$$\Rightarrow 3x - 4x - 28 + 24 = 0$$

$$\Rightarrow -x = 4 \Rightarrow x = -4.$$

By plugging in the value of $x = -4$, in $y = 2x + 14$, we get,

$$y = 2x + 14 \Rightarrow y = 2 \times -4 + 14 \Rightarrow y = -8 + 14 = 6 \Rightarrow y = 6$$

So, $x = -4$, and $y = 6$.

Q3.

$$2x^2 + 7x + 3 = 0$$

Split the middle term $7x$ in two parts such that the product of the parts equals to $2x^2 \times 3 = 6x^2$.

$2x^2 + 7x + 3 = 0$

$\Rightarrow 2x^2 + 6x + x + 3 = 0$; splitting $7x$ into $6x$ and x works as $6x \times x = 6x^2$; though $7x$ can be split into $4x$ and $3x$, $4x \times 3x \neq 6x^2$.

Taking $2x$ common from first two terms, we get,

$2x(x + 3) + 1(x + 3) = 0$

Taking $(x + 3)$ common, we get,

$(x + 3)(2x + 1) = 0$

Product of two terms would be 0, if either of the term is 0. So, either $x + 3 = 0$ or $2x + 1 = 0$.

If $x + 3 = 0 \Rightarrow x = -3$ and if $2x + 1 = 0 \Rightarrow x = -\dfrac{1}{2}$.

So, $x = -3$ or $-\dfrac{1}{2}$.

Q4.

This is indeed a quadratic equation though it does not look like one as we do not see a squared term; however the equation can be solved by applying the concept of quadratic equation.

Say $\sqrt{x} = y$, then the equation becomes $y^2 - 3y + 2 = 0$. It is a quadratic equation. Let's solve this.

$y^2 - 3y + 2 = 0$

$y^2 - 2y - y + 2 = 0$

$y(y - 2) - 1(y - 2) = 0$

$(y - 2)(y - 1) = 0$

So, $y = 2$ or 1.

Or, $\sqrt{x} = 2$ or 1 or $x = 4$ or 1.

Q5.

By now you may be convinced that it a quadratic equation. Let us make it look like one.

$x^{2/3} + x^{1/3} - 2 = 0$

$\Rightarrow (x^{1/3})^2 + x^{1/3} - 2 = 0$

Say $x^{1/3} = y$, then the equation becomes $y^2 + y - 2 = 0$.

Now solving $y^2 + y - 2 = 0$ should be a cake walk for you!

$y^2 + y - 2 = 0$

$\Rightarrow y^2 + 2y - y - 2 = 0$

$y^2 + 2y - y - 2 = 0$

$\Rightarrow y(y + 2) - 1(y + 2) = 0$

$\Rightarrow (y + 2)(y - 1) = 0.$

So, $y = -2$ or 1.

Or, $x^{1/3} = -2$ or 1

$x^{1/3} = -2$ or $1 \Rightarrow x = (-2)^3$ or 1^3

$x = -8$ or 1.

Let us check whether the values calculated are correct. Let us check for $x = -8$.

By plugging in the value of $x = -8$ in the equation $x^{2/3} + x^{1/3} - 2 = 0$, we get,

$(-8)^{2/3} + (-8)^{1/3} - 2 = 0$

$(-2^3)^{2/3} + (-2^3)^{1/3} - 2 = 0$

$(-2)^{3 \times 2/3} + (-2^{3 \times 1/3}) - 2 = 0$

$(-2)^2 + (-2^1) - 2 = 0$

$4 - 2 - 2 = 0 \Rightarrow 0 = 0$. The value calculated is correct.

Q6.

We know that for a quadratic equation $ax^2 + bx + c = 0$ will have equal roots if the discriminant $\Delta = b^2 - 4ac = 0$.

Here, $a = 1, b = 2(m - 4) = 2m - 8$, and $c = 2m$.

So, $\Delta = b^2 - 4ac = (2m - 8)^2 - 4.1.2m = 0$

$4m^2 - 32m + 64 - 8m = 0$

$4m^2 - 40m + 64 = 0$

$4(m^2 - 10m + 16) = 0$

$m^2 - 10m + 16 = 0$

$m^2 - 8m - 2m + 16 = 0$

$m(m - 8) - 2(m - 8) = 0$

$(m - 8)(m - 2) = 0$

or, $m = 8$ or 2.

Q7.

$(4x - 1)^2 = 81$.
Taking the root of both the sides, we get $\sqrt{(4x - 1)^2} = \sqrt{81} \Rightarrow (4x - 1) = \pm 9$.

Remember that square root of any number always takes $\pm$ values.

Taking $+9$ first as the value, we get $(4x - 1) = 9 \Rightarrow x = 5/2$.

Now, Taking -9, we get $(4x - 1) = -9 \Rightarrow x = -2$.

So, $= 5/2$ or -2.

Q8.

$(a - 3)(a + 2) = (a + 3)(a - 2)$

$\Rightarrow a^2 + 2a - 3a - 6 = a^2 - 2a + 3a - 6$

$\Rightarrow -a = a$

$\Rightarrow 2a = 0 \Rightarrow a = 0$.

So a will have only one unique value. Note that the answer is 'One' and not '0'. '0' is the value of a, whereas the question asks us: how many unique values a can have?

Seeing a quadratic equation, one must not jump to a conclusion that the variable will necessary have two values!

Q9.

$$a^3 - a^2 - a + 1 = 0$$

$$\Rightarrow a^2(a - 1) - 1(a - 1) = 0$$

$$\Rightarrow (a - 1)(a^2 - 1) = 0$$

$$\Rightarrow (a - 1)(a - 1)(a + 1) = 0$$

$$\Rightarrow a = \pm 1.$$

There are only two values of a : 1 or -1. The answer is: 'Two'. Again, seeing a cubic equation, one must not jump to a conclusion that the variable will necessarily have three values!

6.10 Absolute numbers

Q1.

$$|10x| - 20 = 0$$

$$\Rightarrow |10x| = 20$$

$$\Rightarrow |x| = 20/10 = 2$$

$$\Rightarrow |x| = 2$$

$$\Rightarrow x = \pm 2.$$

Q2.

$$\left[\frac{-|-3| \times -|3|}{(-|-3|)^2} \right]$$

$$= \left[\frac{-3 \times -3}{(-3)^2} \right]$$

$$= \frac{9}{9} = 1.$$

Q3.

$|2x - 5| = 8$ means that either $2x - 5 = +8$ or $2x - 5 = -8$

If $2x - 5 = +8$, then $2x = 8 + 5 = 13 => x = 13/2$.

And if $2x - 5 = -8$, then $2x = -8 + 5 = -3 => x = -3/2$.

So, $x = 13/2$ or $-3/2$.

6.11   Inequalities

Q1.

The set of values for the inequality: $1 \le x < 3$ is infinite numbers.: {1, 1.1, 1.11, 1.111, 2, 2.345,...}; do not assume that x is an integer until stated. So x may have infinite number of values.

Q2.

Since LHS of the inequity $\frac{1}{p}$ is greater than 1, hence p must be positive.

We can manipulate the inequality as $\left(\frac{1}{p} \times p\right) > 1 \times p => 1 > p$; since we know that p is a positive number, we can multiply both the sides of inequity with a positive number; had it been not known we cannot do it, so considering p as positive, the range of p would be $0 < p < 1$.

Q3.

a. $ab > 0$

Inequality $ab > 0$ suggests that the product of a, and b is positive, it can be positive in two ways:

1. either both a, and b are positive

or

2. both a, and b are negative.

So, $a > 0$ and $b > 0$, **or** $a < 0$ and $b < 0$.

b. $ab < 0$

Inequality $ab < 0$ suggests that the product of a, and b is negative, it can be negative in two ways: either a is positive and b is negative or vice-versa.

So, $a > 0$ and $b < 0$, **or** $a < 0$ and $b > 0$.

c. $ab = 0$

Either $a = 0$ or/and $b = 0$.

d. $\dfrac{a}{b} > 0$

The results are same as (a). The inequality $\dfrac{a}{b} > 0$ suggests that the division of a, and b is positive, it can be positive in two ways:

1. either both a, and b are positive or

2. both a, and b are negative.

e. $\dfrac{a}{b} < 0$

The results are same as (b). The inequality $\dfrac{a}{b} < 0$ suggests suggests that the division of a, and b is negative, it can be negative in two ways: either a is positive and b is negative or vice-versa.

Q4.

$$=> |2x-1| < 5 \begin{cases} 2x - 1 < 5 \\ \\ 2x - 1 > -5; \text{ reverse the sign of inequality when you consider its negative value.} \end{cases}$$

$$=> |2x - 1| < 5 \begin{cases} 2x - 1 < 5 => 2x < 6 => x < 3. \\ \\ 2x - 1 > -5 => 2x > -4 => x > -2. \end{cases}$$

So, the range for x is $-2 < x < 3$.

Q5.

$|x + 2| < 7$

=> $|x + 2| < 7$ means that $-7 < x + 2 < 7$

=> $-7 - 2 < x < 7 - 2$; subtracting 2 from each term

=> $-9 < x < 5$.

Q6.

$|1 - 2x| < 9$

$|1 - 2x| < 9$ means that $-9 < 1 - 2x < 9$

$-10 < -2x < 8$; Subtracting 1 from each term

$5 > x > -4$; Dividing each term by -2. The sign of inequality will change when we multiply or divide terms of inequalities.

So, $-4 < x < 5$.

Q7.

$$\frac{5x - 1}{-6} \le \frac{1 - 2x}{3}$$

$$\frac{5x - 1}{-\overset{2}{\cancel{6}}} \le \frac{1 - 2x}{\cancel{3}}$$

=> $$\frac{5x - 1}{-2} \le 1 - 2x$$

$\left(\frac{5x - 1}{-2}\right) \times -2 \ge -2 \times (1 - 2x)$; Sign of inequality will reverse as we multiplied it with a negative number '-2'.

$\left(\frac{5x - 1}{\cancel{-2}}\right) \times \cancel{-2} \ge -2 \times (1 - 2x)$;

$5x - 1 \geq -2 + 4x => 5x - 4x \geq -2 + 1 => x \geq -1.$

Alternatively

$\dfrac{5x - 1}{-6} \leq \dfrac{1 - 2x}{3}$ can be written as $-\dfrac{5x}{6} + \dfrac{1}{6} \leq \dfrac{1}{3} - \dfrac{2x}{3}$

$=> -\dfrac{5x}{6} + \dfrac{2x}{3} \leq \dfrac{1}{3} - \dfrac{1}{6}$

$=> \dfrac{-5x + 4x}{\cancel{6}} \leq \dfrac{2 - 1}{\cancel{6}}$

$=> -x \leq 1$

$=> x \geq -1.$

Q8.

This is 'Could be true' type of questions. Even if the option is true for only one circumstance, it is the correct answer. 'Could be true' type of questions are different from 'Must be true' type of questions, in which the condition given must be true for all the circumstances.

I. $x^2 < 2x$: For $1 < x < 2$, the inequality $x^2 < 2x$ is true, else not. Say $x = 1/2$, then $(1/2)^2 < 2.(1/2) => 1/4 < 1$; it's true.

   Alternatively, in case of inequality, if x is a positive number which is true in the given inequality($1 < x < 3$), then we can cancel x from both the sides. So, $x^{\cancel{2}} < 2x => x < 2$. $x < 2$ is within the range of $1 < x < 3$, so option (I) is correct.

II. $x^2 = 2x => x = 2; x = 2$ is within the range of $1 < x < 3$, so option (II) is also correct. We must not even consider $x = 0$ as $x = 0$ is out of range of given constraints $1 < x < 3$.

III. $x^2 > 2x => x^{\cancel{2}} > 2x => x > 2$; Similarly, $x > 2$ is within the range of $1 < x < 3$, so option (III) is also correct.

The correct answer is option E.

Q9.

$ab^2c < 0$ suggests that LHS of the inequality: ab^2c is negative. Since b^2 is always positive irrespective of b being positive or negative, hence we cannot deduce whether b is positive or negative.

So, ab^2c is negative because ac is negative or $ac < 0$. This implies that either $a < 0$ and $c > 0$ or $a > 0$ and $c < 0$.

So, $ab^2c < 0$ only suggests that a, and c have opposite signs.

Q10.

The direction of both the inequalities must match. Currently, the directions of inequalities: $8 < x < 3$ and $4 < y < 6$ are opposite. $4 < y < 6$ can be written as $-4 > -y > -6$.

Adding the inequalities, we get...

$$\begin{aligned} 8 > \quad & x \quad > 3 \\ (+)\; -4 > & -y \quad > -6 \\ \hline 4 > & x - y > -3 \\ \hline \end{aligned}$$

So the range of $(x - y)$ is $4 > x - y > -3$.

Q11.

$x + y = x + x + 4 = 2x + 4$, so basically we have to calculate the greatest possible value of $(2x + 4)$.

$6 < x < 12$ can written as $12 < 2x < 24$ and then as $(12 + 4) < 2x + 4 < (24 + 4)$

$\Rightarrow 16 < 2x + 4 < 28 \Rightarrow 16 < x + y < 28$.

It is clear that the greatest possible **integer** value of $x + y$ would be 27.

Had you done in the following way:

The greatest possible **integer** value of $x = 11$, and the greatest possible **integer** value of $y = 11 + 4 = 15$, then the answer would have been $11 + 15 = 26$, which would have been wrong.

Q12.

$x^2 > -6x - 5$

$x^2 + 6x + 5 > 0 \Rightarrow x^2 + 5x + x + 5 > 0 \Rightarrow x(x + 5) + 1(x + 5) > 0 \Rightarrow (x + 5)(x + 1) > 0.$

$(x + 5)(x + 1)$ would be positive if either both $(x + 5)$ and $(x + 1)$ are negative or both are positive.

It is clear that $(x + 5)$ and $(x + 1)$ are positive if $x > -1$.

And, $(x + 5)$ and $(x + 1)$ are negative if $x < -5$.

So, $x > -1$ or $x < -5$.

Q13.

$x^2 > 6x - 5$

$x^2 - 6x + 5 > 0 => x^2 - 5x - x + 5 > 0 => x(x - 5) - 1(x - 5) > 0 => (x - 5)(x - 1) > 0.$

$(x - 5)(x - 1)$ would be positive if either both $(x - 5)$ and $(x - 1)$ are negative or both are positive.

It is clear that $(x - 5)$ and $(x - 1)$ are positive if $x < 1$.

And, $(x - 5)$ and $(x - 1)$ are negative if $x > 5$.

So, $x < 1$ or $x > 5$.

6.12 Percents

Q1.

Let us translate this mathematically: $24 = 8\%$ of x; say the number is x.

$$=> 24 = \frac{8}{100} \times x$$

$$=> x = \frac{24 \times 100}{8} = 300.$$

$$=> x = 300$$

Q2.

Say, he examines x number of screws, so 0.03% of $x = 300$, or $x = 1,000,000$ screws.

Q3.

$x\%$ of 17 = 30% of 289.

$x\% \times 17 = 30\% \times 289$.

$x\% \times \cancel{17} = 30\% \times \cancel{289}^{\,17}$.

$x = 510$

Q4.

Instead of calculating the discount and deducting it from \$800, it is better we calculate 60% of \$800: (100% – 40%) of the final price. So 60% of \$800 = $\dfrac{60}{100} \times 800 = \$480$.

Q5.

$\%\,\text{loss} = \dfrac{\text{SP} - \text{CP}}{\text{CP}} \times 100\% = \dfrac{100 - 120}{120} \times 100\% = -16.67\%$; profit or loss are always based on Cost Price and not on Sales Price.

Q6.

The Marked Price would be 100 + 20 = \$120.

$\%\,\text{Discount} = \dfrac{\text{Discount}}{\text{Marked Price}} \times 100\% = \dfrac{20}{120} \times 100\% = 16.67\%$.

Q7.

Say $Y = 100$, then $X = (100 + 110)\%$ of 100 = 210. Note that: Y is not more by 10%, it is more by 110%.

Given is: $Z = X - 10\%$ of $X = 100\%$ of $X - 10\%$ of $X = 90\%$ of 210 = 189.

Say X is $p\,\%$ of Z, then $p = \dfrac{X}{Z} \times 100\% => p = \dfrac{210}{189} \times 100\% = 111.11\%$.

Q8.

Say Number = N.

$N_1 = 1.20N$; N_1 is the number after the increase. Increasing an number by 20% can better be done by making it 1.20 times.

$N_2 = 0.80N_1 = 0.80 \times 1.20N = 0.96N = 96\%$ of N; N_2 is the number after the decrease. Decreasing an number by 20% can better be done by making it 0.80 times. Remember that the decrease will effect on N_1 and not on N.

The resulting number is not the same as the original number, it decreased by 4%.

What if the number were decreased first, and then increased later?

Well the result would have been the same: 4% decrease!

Q9.

Instead of solving it with a traditional approach, you can apply See-Saw technique discussed earlier in the book.

Step 1: Convert % into fraction. $25\% = \dfrac{1}{4}$;

Step 2: Add '1' to the denominator of the fraction. $\dfrac{1}{4+1} = \dfrac{1}{5}$;

Step 3: Convert the fraction into %. $\dfrac{1}{5} = 20\%$.

The shopkeeper should offer a discount of 20% so that he does not run into losses.

6.13   Ratio & Proportion

Q1.

We know that "Product of middle terms = Product of extreme terms".

$5 \times x = 0.25 \times 4 \Rightarrow 5x = 1/4 \times 4 \Rightarrow 5x = 1 \Rightarrow x = 1/5$.

Q2.

Let the third number be 100.

Then, first number = 120% of 100 = 120.

Second number = 150% of 100 = 150.

Ratio of first two numbers = $120 : 150 = 12 : 15 = 4 : 5$.

Q3.

Given ratio can be simplified as $\dfrac{1}{2} : \dfrac{2}{3} : \dfrac{3}{4} = 6 : 8 : 9$.

Third part $= 529 \times \dfrac{9}{6 + 8 + 9} = 529 \times \dfrac{9}{23} = 207$.

Q4.

Given is: $\dfrac{3}{5}$ of A's amount $= \dfrac{2}{5}$ of B's amount

Or, $\left(\dfrac{3}{\cancel{5}}\right) A = \left(\dfrac{2}{\cancel{5}}\right) B => 3A = 2B$.

A : B = 2 : 3 on ratio scale.

Actual scale Ratio scale
A : B : A+B :: A : B : A+B
? : ? : 240 :: 2 : 3 : 5

So, $A = \dfrac{240}{5} \times 2 = 96$ & $B = \dfrac{240}{5} \times 3 = 144$.

Q5.

Let the numbers be $3x$ and $5x$; where x is a common factor between the numbers.

Then, $\dfrac{3x - 9}{5x - 9} = \dfrac{12}{23}$

$=> 23(3x - 9) = 12(5x - 9) => 9x = 99 => x = 11$.

The larger number $= 5x = (5 \times 11) = 55$.

Q6.

Simply plug in the ratio values of $A, B,$ and C.

$= \dfrac{A}{B} : \dfrac{B}{C} : \dfrac{C}{A} = \dfrac{2}{3} : \dfrac{3}{4} : \dfrac{2}{1}$

$= 8 : 9 : 24$.

Q7.

Quantity of milk $= 60 \times \dfrac{2}{3}$ liters $= 40$ liters.

Quantity of water in the mixture = (60 – 40) liters = 20 liters.

New ratio of milk : water needed = 1 : 2 (Reversed)

Let the quantity of water to be added further be x liters.

Then, milk : water = $\dfrac{40}{20+x}$

Now, $\dfrac{40}{20+x} = \dfrac{1}{2} \Rightarrow 20 + x = 80 \Rightarrow x = 60$.

Quantity of water to be added = 60 liters.

Alternate approach

Since the revised ratio of milk and water is 1 : 2, and milk is not added, it remains 40 liters as before,

$\Rightarrow 40 = \left[\dfrac{1}{2+1}\right]$ of new mixture

So, the new mixture = $40 \times \dfrac{3}{1} = 120$ liters, or quantity of water = 120 – 40 = 80 liters. It means that quantity of water added = 80 – 20 = 60 liters.

Q8.

Given is: $A : B :: 2 : 3, B : C :: 2 : 3$, and $A + B + C = 196$.

B has two values on ratio scale: '3' and '2', we must have a unique value for B in the ratio of $A : B : C$.

Let us take B as '3' on ratio scale, then $B : C :: 2 : 3 = 3 : \left(\dfrac{3}{2} \times 3\right) = 3 : \dfrac{9}{2}$. Not that C changes to $\dfrac{9}{2}$.

So, $A : B : C = 2 : 3 : \dfrac{9}{2} \Rightarrow A : B : C = 4 : 6 : 9$.

Third number = $190 \times \left(\dfrac{9}{4+6+9}\right) = 190 \times \left(\dfrac{9}{19}\right) = 90$.

Q9.

A's new salary = $\dfrac{115}{100} \times 2k = \dfrac{23}{10}k$; whether k is a common factor among the salaries.

B's new salary = $\dfrac{110}{100} \times 3k = \dfrac{33}{10}k$

C's new salary $= \dfrac{120}{100} \times 5k = 6k$

New ratio $= \dfrac{23k}{10} : \dfrac{33k}{10} : 6k = 23 : 33 : 60.$

Q10.

Let the numbers be $2x, 3x$ and $5x$.

Then, $(2x)^2 + (3x)^2 + (5x)^2 = 1862$

$=> 4x^2 + 9x^2 + 25x^2 = 1862$

$=> 38x^2 = 1368$

$=> x^2 = 36 => x = 6.$

$=> $ First number $= 2x = 2.6 = 12.$

6.14   Simple Interest

Q1.

$$\text{SI} = \dfrac{P * r * t}{100}$$

$$=> \ \text{SI} = \dfrac{8000 * 50/3 * 27/12}{100}$$

$$=> \ \text{SI} = \dfrac{8000^{80\ 20} * 50 * 27^{9\ 3}}{3 * 12^{3} * 100} = \$3000.$$

$$=> \ \text{SI} = \$3000.$$

Q2.

$$SI = \dfrac{P * r * t}{100} => P = \dfrac{SI * 100}{r * t}$$

By applying above formula we can easily solve this question, as we are already having the simple interest.

$$\Rightarrow P = \frac{1230 * 100}{6 * 5} \Rightarrow P = \$4100.$$

Q3.

Let the sum 'P' be \$100, so it becomes 'A = \$400' in 15 years or SI= 400 − 100 = \$300.

Now, $r = \dfrac{SI * 100}{P * t}$

$$\Rightarrow r = \frac{300 * 100}{100 * 15} = 20\%.$$

$$\Rightarrow r = 20\%.$$

Q4.

Gain = $\left(\dfrac{P * r_1 * t}{100}\right) - \left(\dfrac{P * r_2 * t}{100}\right)$; where $P = 5000$, $t = 2$, $r_1 = 25/4\%$, and $r_2 = 4\%$.

$$\Rightarrow \text{Gain} = \left(\frac{5000 \times 25/4 \times 2}{100}\right) - \left(\frac{5000 \times 4 \times 2}{100}\right) = (625 - 400) = \$225.$$

$$\Rightarrow \text{Gain} = \$225.$$

Q5.

From question we can conclude that $2200 = \dfrac{P_1 * r * t_1}{100} + \dfrac{P_2 * r * t_2}{100}$; rate is the same for both B and C.

$$\Rightarrow 2200 = \frac{5000 * r * 2}{100} + \frac{3000 * r * 4}{100}$$

$$\Rightarrow 2200 = 100r + 120r \Rightarrow 2200 = 220r \Rightarrow r = 10\%.$$

6.15 Compound Interest

Q1.

We know that $A = P(1 + \dfrac{r}{100})^n$; where A = Amount, P = Principal or Sum.

$A = 7500(1 + \frac{4}{100})^2$

$=> 7500 \left(\frac{26}{25}\right)^2$

$=> 7500 \times \frac{26}{25} \times \frac{26}{25}$

$=> \$8112.$

So, compound interest $= A - P = 8112 - 7500 = \$612.$

Q2.

$CI = A - P$

$CI = P \left(1 + \frac{r}{100}\right)^n - P$

$=> 4000 \left(1 + \frac{10}{100}\right)^2 - 4000$

$=> 4000 \left(\frac{11}{10} * \frac{11}{10} - 1\right)$

$=> 4000(1.21 - 1)$

$=> \$840.$

So, SI = 1/2 of CI $= \frac{840}{2} = 420$

Or, P $= \frac{SI * 100}{r * t}$

$= \frac{420 * 100}{3 * 8}$

$P = \$1750.$

Q3.

$$SI = \frac{P * 4 * 2}{100} = \frac{2}{25}P$$

$$CI = A - P$$

$$CI = P\left(1 + \frac{4}{100}\right)^2 - P$$

$$= \frac{676P}{625} - P$$

$$= \frac{51P}{625}$$

As, C.I. — S.I = 1

$$=> \frac{51P}{625} - \frac{2P}{25} = 1$$

$$=> \frac{51P - 50P}{625} = 1$$

$$=> P = \$625.$$

Alternate approach

It is to be noted that for the first year there is no difference between SI & CI. CI start increasing compared to SI from the second year onwards.

In the question, the difference between CI and SI amounting to $1/- for two years is due to the INTEREST on first year SI for one year.

$$1 = \frac{SI_{I\ yr.} \times 4\% \times 1^{st}\ yr.}{100} => SI_{I\ yr.} = 25/-$$

Again, $SI_{I\ yr.} = 25 = \dfrac{P \times 4\% \times 1}{100} => P = 625/-$.

Q4.

Let the principal be $1 for 1 year when compounded half yearly; so $n = 1 * 2 = 2$ periods, Rate $r = 20/2 = 10\%$ half yrly.

$$A = P\left(1 + \frac{r/2}{100}\right)^{2n} \quad \text{Amount } A = 1\left(1 + \frac{10}{100}\right)^2 = (1.1)^2 = 1.21.$$

So, Effective rate annual rate of interest $= (1.21 - 1) \times 100\% = 21\%$ p.a.

Q5.

It is to be noted that the difference between simple interest and compound interest is that: in case of SI, the interest for any year is calculated on the fixed sum invested initially, whereas in case of CI, the interest for each subsequent year is calculated on the amount of the previous year.

In the question, 840 is the amount for the 4th year and 800 is the amount for the 3rd year, which means that $840 - 800 = 40$ is the interest for the 4th year (one year) on the amount \$800.

So, $r = \dfrac{SI * 100}{P * t}$

$=> r = \dfrac{40 * 100}{800 * 1}$

$=> r = 5\%$.

Alternate approach

$\dfrac{\text{Amount}_{n^{th}\ yr.}}{\text{Amount}_{(n-1)^{th}\ yr.}} = 1 + \dfrac{\text{Rate}}{100}$

So, $\dfrac{840}{800} = 1.05$; or Rate $= 5\%$.

6.16   Functions

Q1.

Since $f(x) = 2x - 7$, hence $f(2x - 6) = 2.(2x - 6) - 7 = 4x - 12 - 7 = 4x - 19$: replacing '$x$' with $2x - 6$.

Now, $3f(x) - 3 = f(2x - 6) => 3.(2x - 7) - 3 = 4x - 19$; substituting the values of $f(x) = 2x - 7$ and $f(2x - 6)$.

We get, $6x - 21 - 3 = 4x - 19 => x = 5/2$.

Q2.

$[25] = -|\sqrt{25}| = -5$; as 25 is an odd number.

And, $[10] = \dfrac{10}{5} = 2$; as 10 is an even number.

So, $[25] * [10] = -5 \times 2 = -10$.

Q3.

Set of integers less than -2.2 are {-3, -4, -5,....}; among them, the greatest is -3, so, $[-2.2] = -3$.

Similarly, set of integers less than 2.6 are {2, 1, 0, -1,....}; among them, the greatest is 2, so, $[2.6] = 2$.

Similarly, set of integers less than 6.2 are {6, 5, 4,....}; among them the greatest is 6, so, $[6.2] = 6$.

So, $[-2.2] + [2.6] + [6.2] = -3 + 2 + 6 = 5$.

Q4.

$a\#c = \dfrac{(a+c)}{(a^2+c^2)} = 0 => a+c = 0 \times (a^2+c^2) => a+c = 0 => c = -a$.

Q5.

Say $f(x) = y$, then we can say that $f(y) = -1$ and deduce $f(y) = \dfrac{2y}{2y-1} = -1 =>$ $-2y+1 = 2y => y = 1/4$.

Again, $y = f(x) = \dfrac{1}{4} => \dfrac{2x}{2x-1} => 2x-1 = 8x => x = -1/6$.

Q6.

$f(g(x)) = \dfrac{2.\left(\dfrac{2x-1}{2x}\right)}{2.\left(\dfrac{2x-1}{2x}\right)-1} = \dfrac{\left(\dfrac{2x-1}{x}\right)}{\left(\dfrac{2x-1}{x}\right)-1} = \dfrac{\left(\dfrac{2x-1}{x}\right)}{\left(\dfrac{2x-1-x}{x}\right)} = \dfrac{2x-1}{x-1}$.

Now, $f(g(x)) = 3 => \dfrac{2x-1}{x-1} = 3 => 2x-1 = 3x-3 => x = 2$.

Q7.

$f(p^2 - 10p + 25)$ can be simplified as $f((p - 5)^2)$.

So, $f(p^2 - 10p + 25) = f((p - 5)^2) = 2.(p - 5)^2 + \sqrt{(p - 5)^2}$

Taking $\sqrt{(p - 5)^2} = p - 5$, we get $f(p^2 - 10p + 25) = 2p^2 - 20p + 50 + p - 5 = 2p^2 - 19p + 45$.

Taking $\sqrt{(p - 5)^2} = 5 - p$, we get $f(p^2 - 10p + 25) = 2p^2 - 20p + 50 - p + 5 = 2p^2 - 21p + 55$.

$\Rightarrow f(p^2 - 10p + 25) = 2p^2 - 19p + 45$ or $2p^2 - 21p + 55$.

Chapter 7

Speak to Us

Have a Question?

Please email your questions to info@manhattanreview.com. We will be happy to answer you. You questions can be related to a concept, an application of a concept, an explanation of a question, a suggestion for an alternate approach, or anything else you wish to ask regarding the GRE.

Please do mention the page number when quoting from the book.

GRE - Resources from ETS

· *Official Guide*: It is one of the best resource to prepare for the GRE revised General test. It is a complete GRE book with everything you need to do your best on the test — and move toward your graduate or business school degree. It includes a couple of full-length practice test and two simulated, computer-based GRE practice tests., which help you measure your capability beforehand. The book also includes a *POWERPREP II* CD.

· *GRE Big Book*: It is a big fat book and includes 27 previously administered full-length tests. There are over 5000 actual ETS questions and answers. The strategies and tips to crack the computerized GRE is worth reading.

Manhattan Admissions

You are a unique candidate with unique experience.
We help you to sell your story to the admissions committee.

Manhattan Admissions is an educational consulting firm that guides academic candidates through the complex process of applying to the world's top educational programs. We work with applicants from around the world to ensure that they represent their personal advantages and strength well and get our clients admitted to the world's best business schools, graduate programs and colleges.

We will guide you through the whole admissions process:

- ☑ Personal Assessment and School Selection
- ☑ Definition of your Application Strategy
- ☑ Help in Structuring your Application Essays
- ☑ Unlimited Rounds of Improvement
- ☑ Letter of Recommendation Advice
- ☑ Interview Preparation and Mock Sessions
- ☑ Scholarship Consulting

To schedule a free 30-minute consulting and candidacy evaluation session or read more about our services, please visit or call:

 www.manhattanadmissions.com   +1.212.334.2500

Made in the USA
San Bernardino, CA
11 November 2015